Wild flowers
of Cyprus

George Sfikas

Wild flowers of Cyprus

With 215 illustrations in colour by the Author

EFSTATHIADIS GROUP

Efstathiadis Group S.A.
Agiou Athanasiou Street,
GR - 145 65 Anixi, Attikis

ISBN 960 226 432 2

ISBN 960 226 266 4

Printed and bound in Greece by Efstathiadis Group S.A.

Land of lemon and olive trees
Land of joy's embrace
Land of Pine and Cypress trees,
of valour and of love
Goldengreen leaf
cast on the sea.

Land of the withered meadow
Land of the embittered Virgin (sorrowful)
Land of the breeze of unjust loss,
of violent times and of fire
Goldengreen leaf
cast on the sea.

Land of girls who smile
Land of boys who rejoice
Land of myrrh's greetings
Cyprus of love and dream
Goldengreen leaf
cast on the sea.

L. Malenis

CONTENTS

Introduction The island's history 7

Geography 11

Geology 16

Climate 16

Vegetation and Flora 18

Phytogeographical sub-divisions 24

Botanical investigations 28

The botanical paradises of Cyprus 30

List of plants endemic to Cyprus 48

Glossary 68

Key to families 73

Families 90

Index of Latin Names 316

Bibliography 320

INTRODUCTION
THE ISLAND'S HISTORY

In prehistoric times Cyprus (Kípros) was an uninhabited island, covered in thick forests and full of wild animals. The first traces of human habitation found to date correspond roughly to the 6th millennium BC. It would appear that not until then were men from the countries around the Mediterranean able to cross the sea in primitive boats and rafts.

The first inhabitants of Cyprus, known as Eteocypriots, came from the nearby coasts of Asia Minor and the Middle East. By the third millennium BC the Eteocypriots had discovered and were using the island's rich deposits of copper.

Around 1500 BC, Mycenean merchants from Greece began settling in Cyprus. They transplanted Greek culture onto the island. At the same time Cyprus became the target of settlers from nearby Phoenicia (now Lebanon), also settled on the island, particularly after the 10th century BC.

By Homeric times Cyprus had been Hellenised to a great degree; this was when the island became linked to Greece, linguistically and culturally. Later the island was conquered by the Assyrians, the Egyptians and the Persians, but it always retained its Greek identity and culture.

During the time of the conquests of Alexander the Great (336-323 BC), Cyprus became part of the vast realm of the Macedonians. After the break-up of the Macedonian Empire, it came under the rule of the Ptolemies, the Macedonian kings of Egypt. In 58 BC the Romans finally conquered it, and Cyprus was transformed into a tiny province of the vast Roman Empire.

In Byzantine times Cyprus became part of the Eastern Roman Empire (the Byzantine state) and thus became linked to Byzantinum

One of the many extremely ancient rock-tombs in Cyprus. Right: the Kiko Monastery, in the Troodos Range. Western influences are apparent in its architecture.

in language, religion and culture. Arabs attacked the island frequently, but were never able to conquer it.

After many centuries of Byzantine rule, or misrule, Cyprus was conquered in 1191 by Richard the Lionhearted. Richard ceded it to the Frankish king of Jerusalem Guy de Lusignan, who had helped him win it. This marked the beginning of Frankish rule by the autonomous Frankish house of Lusignan.

After almost three centuries of administration by the Franks, Cyprus passed into Venetian hands in 1489. Scarcely a century later, in 1571, the Turks occupied it. They held it until 1878, when they ceded it to England under a secret treaty, as a temporary base.

In 1914 the British government decided to repeal unilaterally the treaty with Turkey and annexed Cyprus officially to the British

Empire, in accordance with the time-tested law of "Might makes right".

After many struggles for self-determination, the Cypriots forced the British to withdraw from the island in 1959; British presence was reduced to only a few bases. The independent Cypriot state founded in 1960 was called the Republic of Cyprus; its president was Archbishop Makarios. Also represented in the government were the Turkish Cypriots, who constituted the island's Moslem minority.

In 1974 an attempt was made by a small minority of ultraright-wingers, with the blessings of the then dictatorial government in Athens, to set up a dictatorship on the island after deposing the government of Archbishop Makarios. Turkey reacted by sending its army to invade Cyprus on the pretext of protecting the Turkish Cypriot minority.

After the invasion, the southern part, the larger of the two, continued to be the lawful Cypriot state, the Republic of Cyprus, recognised by the UN, while the northern part was unlawfully declared a Turkish Cypriot state, recognised only by Turkey who undertook to protect it with its occu-pying forces.

The border between the two parts runs the length of the central plain south of Mórphou and Famagusta (Amóhostos), cutting the capital Nicosia (Lefkossía) in two.

The Turkish invasion did not fail to have an influence on the natural environment. The rapid population increase in the southern sector due to the relocation of thousands of Greek Cypriot refugees, the sudden, often explosive growth of towns in the south like Limassol, whose population and area trebled within twelve years, the division of large flat and seaside areas into building plots and the conversion of the coasts into tourist havens: all these, as would be expected, have had very adverse repercussions on the island's flora and fauna. Luckily for the flora, most of the rare species of plants and those endemic to the island grow

Hundreds of apartment buildings and dozens of hotels have sprung up in Limassol in recent years.

at high altitudes in the island's two large mountain ranges, and thus are not immediately endangered.

GEOGRAPHY

Cyprus with an area of 9.250 square kilometers is the third largest island in the Mediterranean after Sicily and Sardinia. Its length is 226 kilometers and its greatest width 96 kilometers. Its northern coast runs parallel to the coast of Turkey, which is only 72 kilometers from Cape Kormakíti.

The greater part of the east coast lies 160-180 kilometers away from Syria, except for Cape Apóstolos Andreas which is only 105 kilometers away. Lebanon is also quite close; its capital Beirut being 175 kilometers southeast of Cavo Greco.

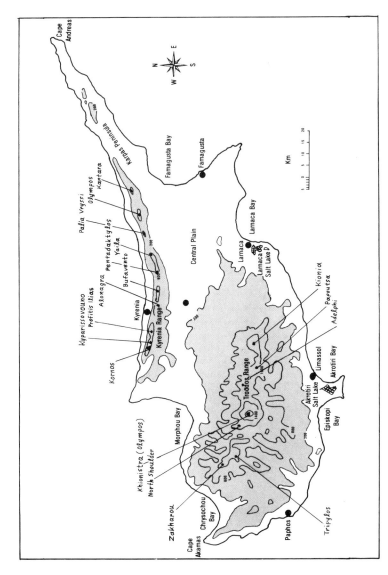

The island is dominated by two mountain ranges which run parallel to each other in a general east-to-west direction; they are separated by a wide plain. In the north the Pendadahtilos Range, also known as the Kyrenia (Kirínia) range, forms a continuous wall which separates the interior from the littoral zone; it begins with Kórnos Peak in the west near Cape Kormakíti and ends in a series of hills in the Karpassía peninsula. The highest peaks in the Pendadahtilos Range are Kiparissóvouno at 1.024 m. and Buffavento at 955 m. There are however many other peaks over 700 m. in height, such as Kórnos at 946 m., Trípa Vounó or Alonagra at 935 m., Giaila at 935 m., Olympus (Ólimbos) at 7.40 m., Prophet Elijah (Profítis Ilías) at 888 m., Palia Vríssi at 819 m., Sina Óros or Kandara at 764 m. and finally Pendadahtilos at 740 m., with its five characteristic summits. It can be seen from a great distance and has justifiably given its name to the whole range.

In the south of Cyprus looms the huge Tróodos Range, whose peaks are almost twice as high as those of Pendadahtilos. The loftiest is Hionístra or Olympus which reaches a height of 1.961 m. Other tall peaks are Papoútsa at 1.554 m., Kiónia or Maheras at 1.423 m., Madarí or Adelfí at 1.612 m., Trípilos at 1.362 m., Zaharoú at 1.212 m., North Shoulder at 1.700 m., Kalifón at 1.158 m. and Stavrópefkos at 1.234 m.

The portion of the island between the two mountain ranges is known as Kendrikí Pediada (Central Plain) or Messaória: In the east it is flatter than in the west, where it undulates up into a series of hills, some of which, such as Xerí and Agía Marína, are over 300 m. in height.

There is also a relatively narrow plain in the southern part of Cyprus, between the coast and the Troodos Range. Even smaller areas of flat and are to be found in the narrow Karpassia peninusula in the northeast corner of the island.

The small torrents, most of which originate in the Troodos Range, could hardly be classed as rivers, since most of them run dry

Opposite page: map of Cyprus.

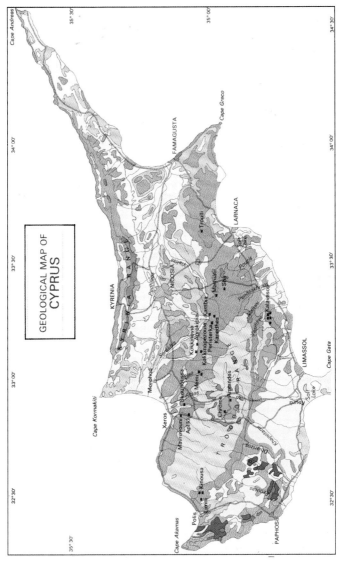

Geological map of Cyprus.

SEDIMENTARY FORMATIONS

	Alluvium	RECENT
	Fanglomerate, Terrace Deposits	PLEISTOCENE
	Nicosia-Athalassa Formations	PLIO-PLEISTOCENE
	Kalavasos, Koronia, Pakhna and Kythrea Formations	MIDDLE-UPPER MIOCENE
	Terra, Lefkara, Ardana-Kalogrea and Lapithos Formations	MAESTRICHTIAN-LOWER MIOCENE
	Moni, Kannaviou and Perapedhi Formations	CAMPANIAN-MAESTRICHTIAN
	Hilarion, Sykhari, Dhikomo and Kantara Formations	PERMO-CARBONIFEROUS TO LOWER CRETACEOUS
	Mamonia Complex	TRIASSIC TO LOWER CRETACEOUS

TROODOS OPHIOLITE (PRE-CAMPANIAN)

	Upper and Lower Pillow Lavas and Basal Group	PILLOW LAVA SERIES
	Diabase	SHEETED DYKE COMPLEX
	Plagiogranite	PLAGIOGRANITE
	Gabbro	GABBRO
	Pyroxenite, Wehrlite, Dunite	⎫
	Harzburgite, Serpentinite	⎬ ULTRAMAFICS
	Serpentinite (Mamonia Complex)	⎭
■	Mine	

Legend of geological map..

during the summer months. The island's longest river is the Pediéos, which flows for 95 kilometers through the Central Plain before emptying into the Bay of Famagusta. There were also some interesting fresh-water marshes near Fassoúri and Limassol (Lemessós); unfortunately, they have been drained. Finally, let us mention the two salt lakes, near Larnaca and Limassol, of tremendous importance for migratory water-birds.

GEOLOGY

Most of the island's coasts are rocky, but there are several sand beaches scattered throughout the littoral zone. Around Famagusta and Karpassia there are sand-hills and flats.

The Pendadahtilos Range of mountains are the island's oldest; they were formed during the Alpine orogenesis and consist of limestone of the Permian, Carboniferous and Cretaceous periods, with interjacent layers of basalt. On their lower slopes we find marl, sandstone and conglomerates of the Miocene. Water is scarce in the area, although there are a few significant springs, near the villages of Lapithos and Karavas, which irrigate great citrus orchards.

Unlike Pendadahtilos, the Troodos Range is volcanic in origin and is made up of serpentine-rock, diabase, gabbro and pillow-lava. The Troodos Range is also younger, and its rocks contain rich mineral deposits, among them asbestos, chromite, iron pyrites and copper pyrites, from which the copper is extracted that made the island rich and powerful from the earliest times.

The Central Plain consists mainly of Flysch, marl and shell-lime stone, while in the areas around Troodos chalk, limestone and gypsum are common.

Of particular interest from a geological standpoint is the Akamas peninsula in the western end of Cyprus, for the great variety of rocks found there and the resulting variety of vegetation.

CLIMATE

The climate of Cyprus is defined as xero-Mediterranean, with cool, wet but short winters and very hot, dry, long summers. Average

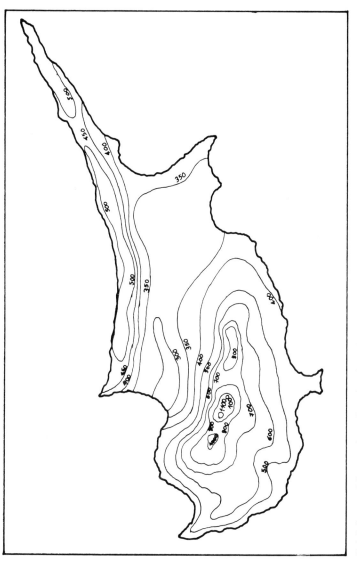

Rainfall map of Cyprus, based on data from the period 1941-70.

annual rainfall is approximately 500 millimeters: most of it occurs between November and March.

Of course, in the Troodos and Pendadahtilos Ranges rainfall is well over the average; on Hionistra Peak, the island's highest, annual rainfall reaches 1.000 millimeters. Less rain falls in the Central Plain. In the region of Paphos in the west, rainfall amounts to only about 254 millimeters annually.

The peaks of the Troodos Range are snow-capped in winter. In the highest places there is continual snow cover from December until the beginning of April, while on the northern slopes of Hionistra the snow often does not melt until May.

VEGETATION AND FLORA

In antiquity, forests in Cyprus were much richer and more extensive than those remaining today. From the writings of Eratosthenes (275-195 BC) one can clearly see that most of the island was forested in those times. Of those forests only a small portion remains today, mainly in the Troodos and Pendadahtilos Ranges; it represents about 17-18% of the island's surface area. The rest of the forests have fallen victim to the activities of man, who for centuries has tried to extend his fields and pastures to the detriment of the forests, by cutting and burning. In the years before World War II, forested areas were even fewer than they are today, chiefly as a result of free, unrestrained grazing of goats. Drastic measures had to be taken and concerted action instituted by the British government of the day to renew the forests, either by allowing them to regenerate naturally or by replanting them. The results of this policy, whose basic aim was to keep goats out of the mountainous zones, can now be seen clearly, when the magnificent pine forests of Troodos are compared to the bare, parched mountains of Crete, where unrestrained activities including overgrazing are still the rule.

The Cypriot government continued the policy of the British administration after 1960. Thus it is typical that fires very seldom break out

Reforestation in the northwestern region of the Troodos Range, which was burned during the Turkish invasion.

in the forests of Cyprus, which belong to the state and consequently do not fall victim to private interests and claims to land.

Nevertheless, we must not overlook errors that have been made. The most serious was that during the last twenty years clumps of trees and whole forests have been planted consisting of species totally foreign to the local flora. Among them are various species of fir and American Sequoias in the mountains, various species of acacia and pine including Pinus halepensis, not indigenous to Cyprus, in the plains. These errors must not be repeated in the future, if we want the forests of Cyprus to retain their ecological balance.

Ascending from sea level to the mountain peaks we may remark the existence of different vegetation according to altitude. The underlying rock also plays a decisive role in determining the

Mediterranean maquis (shrubs) in the region of Akamas.

types of trees, bushes and scrub vegetation which grow above it.

The hills and lower reaches of the mountains were once covered with the shrubs known as "Mediterranean maquis", among them the Greek Strawberry-tree (Arbutus adrachne), the Storax (Styrax officinalis), the Wild Olive-tree (Olea europaea - subsp. oleaster) and the Kerm oak or Holly oak (Quercus coccifera) or with trees adapted to hot climates such as the Carob or Locust tree (Cerato-nia siliqua). Superb examples of maquis survive today on the lower northern slopes of the Pendadahtilos Range, in certain places in the lowest zone of the Troodos Range, on the Akamas peninsula and in various places on the Karpassia peninsula. In other areas the original vegetation has given way either to the Phoenician juniper (Juniperus phoenicea) which can withstand grazing better, or to cultivation or to phrygana.In the highest zone of the Pendadahtilos Range dominant species are the Calabrian pine (Pinus brutia) and indigenous Cypresses

Forest of Calabrian pine (Pinus brutia) in the Troodos Range.

(Cypressus sempervirens). In the Troodos Range at altitudes of between 600 and 1.300 m. Pinus brutia forms large forests, while here and there one may observe the endemic species of oak, Quercus alnifolia. In one particular area, on the slopes of Tripilos Peak, there is a forest of the Cedar endemic to Cyprus, (Cedrus libanii - subsp. brevifolia). This tree has been used for reforestation in other parts of the Troodos Range.

At greater altitudes, in the highest zone of the Troodos Range, there are great forests of Black pine (Pinus nigra - subsp. pallasiana) which stretch almost all the way up to Hionistra Peak, that is up to 1.850 m. At certain places in the Troodos range, such as Madari and Papoutsa Peaks, Great or Greek juniper (Juniperus excelsa) takes over from Black pine; in the upper zone of Hionistra Peak there is a small forest of Stinking juniper (Juniperus foetidissima).

A mixed forest of Cyprus oak (Quercus alnifolia) and Calabrian pine (Pinus brutia) in the northwestern part of the Troodos Range.

In the torrent-beds and gorges of Troodos grow the Oriental plane (Platanus orientalis) and the Asiatic species of Alder, Alnus orientalis, while in the torrent-beds at lower altitudes the Oleander (Nerium oleander) and the Chaste tree (Vitex agnus-castus) are plentiful.

Vegetation on the saltings and the regions around the salt lakes has certain peculiar features. In such places grow plants which can withstand salinity, such as Salicornia fruticosa and Atriplex halimus, accompanied by species not so intimately associated with the sea, like the Giant fennel Ferula communis and the Cardoon Cynara cardungulus and even the semi-indigenous Date palm, Phoenix dactylifera.

Finally, in the central plain, in places not under cultivation, a characteristic type of scrub prevails, whose dominant plant species

Forest of Black pine or Mandópefkos (Pinus nigra ssp. pallasiana) on Hionistra Peak in the Troodos Range. Below: forest of Stinking juniper or Aóratos (Juniperus foetidissima) on Hionistra Peak.

is the Hawthorn, Crataegus azarolus. The same shrub can also be observed in relative abundance on the lower parts of the northern slopes of the Troodos Range.

The flora of Cyprus is one of the richest in the countries of the Eastern Mediterranean; it includes 151 familes of plants, 668 genera and approximately 1.820 species. Many of these species are endemic to the island or have a very limited range in the Eastern Mediterranean. Most rare plants are concentrated in the two mountain ranges and in the Akamas peninsula.

Another feature of the flora of Cyprus is that different plants grow in each of the island's two mountain ranges, due to the completely different composition of their rocks. For example, the species of Rockcress Arabis cypria grows in the Pendadahtilos Range, while the corresponding plant in the Troodos Range is Arabis purpurea, which thrives on serpentine-rock. Likewise, Vicia cypria grows on Pendadahtilos and Vicia lunata on the serpentine of Troodos. We may find the endemic Onosma caespitosum on Pendadahtilos and another endemic, Onosma troodi, on Troodos.

PHYTOGEOGRAPHICAL SUB-DIVISIONS

As regards flora, R.D. Meikle divided Cyprus into eight zones, each with its own pecularities of climate and soil and its own distinctive characteristic vegetation. These zones are as follows:

a) the western end of the island, including the Akamas peninsula. Due to the variety of rocks found there as well as to its relative isolation, it was able to retain an extremely interesting flora which includes many species endemic to Cyprus, such as Alyssum akamasicum, Tulipa cypria, and others.

b) the Troodos Range. Because of its great height, distinctive and

Semi-naturalised Date palm (Phoenix dactylifera) on the shore of the Larnaca salt lake

rare rocks (chiefly serpentine) and relatively undisturbed environment, it has retained many endemic or rare plants, such as Quercus alnifolia, Cedrus libanii - subsp. brevifolia, Alyssum troodi, Alyssum cypricum, Arabis purpurea and many others.

c) the southern region around Limassol. Here are places of exceptional interest like the Akrotíri peninsula with its brackish lake, the marshes around Fassouri which unfortunately have been drained, the serpentine sites near Kakomali and Louvaras, the region around the Stavrovoúni Monastery, etc. In the southern region we may find Alyssum chondrogynum, Linum maritimum, Centaurea veneris, Ipomoea sagittata, Euphorbia thompsonii and other rare plants.

d) the vicinity of Larnaca, in particular Cavo Greco in the southeast part of the island. Here there are also several rare species including Matthiola fruticulosa, Crambe hispanica, Scilla hyacinthoides, Urginea undulata, Hymenolobus procumbens, et al.

e) the eastern section of the Central Plain, Kendriki Pediada, and the southern slopes of the Pendadahtilos Range. Here, too, there are quite a few interesting plant species.

f) the western portion of the Central Plain. This region also has many interesting sites with distinctive flora. Growing on Cape Kormakiti, for example, are Argyrolobium uniflorum, Achillea santolina, Cyclamen graecum, rare in Cyprus, as well as Convolvulus oleifolius - var. pumilus, among others. In the environs of Diório and Mírtou, Tulipa cypria grows, while the gorges south of Peristeróna are also very interesting and have not been fully investigated as yet.

g) The northern slopes and peaks of the Pendadahtilos Range. This is one of the most fascinating regions of the island as far as flora is concerned. Many rare or endemic species grow here,

Map of the phytogeographic divisions of Cyprus

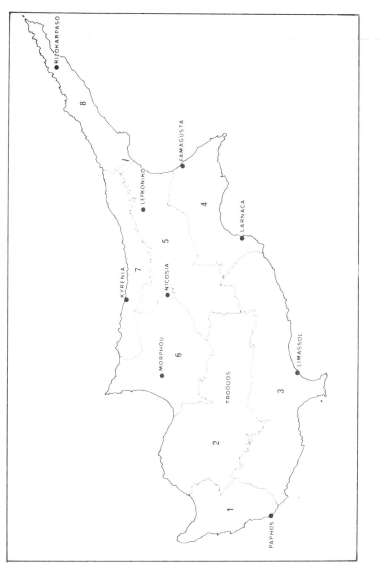

RIZOKARPASO

FAMAGUSTA

LEFKONIKO

LARNACA

KYRENIA

NICOSIA

MORPHOU

LIMASSOL

TROODOS

PAPHOS

8

1

4

5

7

6

2

3

1

among them Dianthus cyprius, Helianthemum obtusifolium, Arabis cypria, and many more.

h) The Karpassia peninsula on the eastern tip of the island. This is another region with interesting flora, including many rare plants, such as Enarthrocarpus arcuatus, Trifolium globosum, Fumaria gaillardotii, and others.

BOTANICAL INVESTIGATIONS

Many botanists and naturalists have visited Cyprus during the last two centuries. Some of them left their mark on the botanical history of the island by discovering numerous new species of plants.

In 1787 the famous English botanist John Sibthorp arrived in Cyprus with his friends John Hawkins and Ferdinand Bauer the painter. They toured the whole island and collected many plant specimens. It has been estimated that Sibthorp collected 313 species of plants which cast only a faint light on the wealth of the flora of Cyprus.

Later the Austrian Karl Geor. Theodor Kotschy visited Cyprus three times, in 1840, 1859 and 1862. He is estimated to have collected 1.050 species of plants, both spermatophytes and pteridophytes.

In 1880 the German Paul Ernst Emil Sintenis and the Italian Gregorio Rigo came to Cyprus. These two famous botanists travelled throughout almost the entire island. However the most significant investigations of the flora of Cyprus were carried out by an English man, Jens Holmboe, in 1905. He published the results of his investigations in 1914 in his book "Studies on the Vegetation of Cyprus".

In 1912 the Armenian Manoog Haradjian investigated the flora of Cyprus, as did Harald Lindberg in 1939. Another important investigator was the Cypriot A. Singrassídis, who studied the flora of Cyprus from 1932 to 1939, creating a rich herbarium. Many of the

The gorges in the Akamas peninsula shelter many rare plants

plants found by Singrassidis were included by A. Jackson and W. Turril in "Additions to the Flora of Cyprus" published by the Kew Bulletin between 1934 and 1939.

Another important investigator was E.W. Kennedy who concentrated her studies on the plants of Troodos and Kyrenia between the years of 1936 and 1955. Finally we must not fail to mention the Englishman P. H. Davis who passed through the island in 1940-41, collected several new species and gave data on the distribution of others which were not at all well known.

Another noteworthy collection is that of G. Mavromoustakis, who mainly studied the plants in the vicinity of Limassol from 1939 to 1948. In her book "Cyprus Trees and Shrubs", published in 1949, E. F. Chapman examined the distribution of woody plants.

In 1973 B. F. Osorio - Tafall and G. Seraphim published their book "List of the Vascular Plants of Cyprus" a complete list of the flora of Cyprus, on the basis of the bibliography existing at that time.

In the meantime the Englishman R. D. Meikle had begun a systematic, long-term study of the flora of Cyprus in 1962, with the aim of publishing a complete "Flora cypriana". In 1977 the first volume, "Flora of Cyprus - Vol 1" appeared, followed by the second volume in 1985.

This two-volume work gives detailed descriptions of all the plants of Cyprus, together with their precise distribution. It also gives data on the habitat and the region in which each species occurs.

THE BOTANICAL PARADISES
OF CYPRUS AND THE NECESSITY
OF PROTECTING THEM

After the publication in 1985 of the second volume of "Flora of Cyprus" which completed this extremely important work of R. D.

The Cedar forest on the western slopes of the Troodos Range

Meikle, we are now in a position to know the precise number of plants of the flora of Cyprus, their distributions and exactly how many of them are endemic to the island. Before this work was published information was rather confused, particularly as regards the existence or non-existence in Cyprus of certain species described years earlier, as well as regards nomenclature and the number of endemics. Moreover, certain endemic plants described by Meikle were discovered by him and consequently are not to be found in previous catalogues.

Using the "Flora of Cyprus" as a basic aid and supplying further information taken from more recent publications as well as data of my own regarding the distribution of certain species, I now find myself in the agreeable position of being able to present a catalogue of the endemic taxa of Cyprus: 121 species, subspecies and varieties, together with their distributions.

I believe that this work constitutes another step in the cataloguing and study of the "Flora Cypriana", which surely could not have been taken if the "Flora of Cyprus" had not preceded it. It is characteristic that in Greece we have not yet been able to catalogue precisely our endemic plants because no complete, authoritative Flora Hellenica exists; it has just begun to be written.

At the same time that I listed the endemics and their distributions, I tried to point out the regions where greatest concentrations of them occur. As one would expect, these regions are habitats of particular value, botanical paradises in need of special protection: It is now common knowledge that in order to save a rare plant species it is not enough to declare it protected; above all its habitat must be preserved.

Some of the botanical paradises of Cyprus are already being protected quite effectively: for example, the peaks of the Troodos Range and in particular Western Troodos. On the other hand, others, like the region of Akamas, are at this moment under severe

Characteristic beach and seaside vegetation at Akamas peninsula.

pressure, mainly for the sake of tourism. Finally, some of the most significant areas where rare endemic plants are concentrated, such as the Kyrenia Range and the region of Karpassia, are at present occupied by Turkey, and their fate rests in her hands.

1. AKAMAS PENINSULA

Local Endemics
Alyssum akamasicum

Endemic to Cyprus
Allium willeanum
Anthemis tricolor
Arenaria rhodia - ssp. cypria
Astragalus cyprius
Ballota integrifolia
Bosea cypria
Carlina involucrata - var. cyprica
Carlina pygmaea
Centaurea veneris
Cyclamen cyprium
Gagea juliae
Gladiolus triphyllus
Helianthemum obtusifolium
Onobrychis venosa
Onopordon cyprium
Onosma fruticosum
Origanum majorana - var. tenuifolium
Phlomis cypria - var. occidentalis
Ptilostemon chamaepeuce - var. cyprius
Rubia laurae
Scutellaria cypria - var. elatior
Sedum cyprium
Sedum porphyreum
Senecio glaucus - ssp. cyprius

View in the Akamas peninsula

Taraxacum aphrogenes
Teucrium macropodioides
Thymus integer
Tulipa cypria

2. TROODOS RANGE

Local Endemics

Acinos troodi
Alyssum troodi
Arabis kennedyae
Arabis purpurea
Astragalus echinus - var. chionistrae
Allium paniculatum - subsp. exaltatum
Brachypodium firmifolium
Cedrus libanii - ssp. brevifolia
Cephalorrhynchus cypricus
Chionodoxa lochiae
Crocus cyprius
Cynoglossum troodi
Cyperus cyprius
Euphorbia cassia - ssp. rigoi
Euphorbia veneris
Genista sphacelata - var. crudelis
Jurinea cypria
Lindbergella sintenisii
Micromeria chionistrae
Minuartia sintenisii
Minuartia subtilis - ssp. filicaulis
Nepeta troodi
Onosma troodi
Origanum cordifolium
Ornithogalum chionophilum
Papaver argemone - ssp. meiklii
Quercus alnifolia

The cedars in the Troodos Range are an endemic subspecies related to the Lebanon cedar

Ranunculus cadmicus - var. cyprius
Ranunculus kykkoënsis
Rosa chionistrae
Salvia willeana
Saponaria cypria
Scariola tetrandra
Scariola viminea
Scilla morrisii
Scutellaria cypria - var. cypria
Sedum microstachium
Silene galataea
Silene gemmata
Silene laevigata
Taraxacum holmboei
Teucrium cyprium - ssp. cyprium
Thlaspi cyprium
Trifolium campestre - var. paphium

Endemic to Cyprus

Acinos exiguus
Allium autumnale
Allium willeanum
Anthemis plutonia
Anthemis tricolor
Arenaria rhodia - ssp. cypria
Asperula cypria
Astragalus cyprius
Bosea cypria
Carlina involucrata - var. cypria
Carlina pygmaea
Centranthus calcitrapa - ssp. orbiculatus
Crocus hartmannianus
Cyclamen cyprium
Dianthus strictus - var. troodi
Gagea juliae

A centuries-old Black pine (Pinus nigra) near Hionistra Peak

Gladiolus triphyllus
Hypericum repens
Odontites cypria
Onopordon cyprium
Onosma fruticosum
Orchis anatolica - var. troodi
Origanum majorana - var. tenuifolium
Orobanche cypria
Petrorhagia kennedyae
Phlomis cypria - var. occidentalis
Pterocephalus multiflorus - ssp. multiflorus
Ptilostemon chamaepeuce - var. cyprius
Rubia laurae
Scabiosa cyprica
Scorzonera troodea
Scutellaria cypria - var. elatior
Sedum cyprium
Teucrium divaricatum - ssp. canescens
Thymus integer
Trifolium pamphylicum - var. dolichodontium

3. PENDADAHTILOS RANGE, REGION OF KYRENIA AND KYTHREA (KITHRÉA)

Local endemics
Agrostis cypricola
Arabis cypria
Brassica hilarionis
Delphinium caseyi
Ferulago cypria
Onosma caespitosum
Origanum syriacum - var. bevanii
Phlomis cypria - var. cypria
Rosularia cypria
Rosularia pallidiflora
Salvia veneris
Sedum lambusae
Sideritis cypria

Dam in the Xeros River Valley in the western part of the Troodos Range. Many rare plants grow in the valleys and gorges of the Troodos Range.

Silene fraudatrix
Teucrium cyprium - ssp. kyreniae

Endemic to Cyprus

Allium autumnale
Allium willeanum
Anthemis tricolor
Asperula cypria
Astragalus cyprius

Ballota integrifolia
Bosea cypria
Centaurea calcitrapa - ssp. angusticeps
Centranthus calcitrapa - ssp. orbiculatus
Crocus hartmannianus
Cyclamen cyprium
Dianthus cyprius

Dianthus strictus - var. troodi
Gagea juliae
Gladiolus triphyllus
Hedysarum cyprium
Helianthemum obtusifolium
Limonium albidum - ssp. cyprium
Odontites cypria
Onobrychis venosa
Onopordon cyprium
Onosma fruticosum
Ophrys kotschyi
Origanum majorana - var. tenuifolium
Phlomis brevibracteata
Pimpinella cypria
Pterocephalus multiflorus - ssp. obtusifolius
Ptilostemon chamaepeuce - var. cyprius
Ranunculus millefoliatus - ssp. leptaleus
Rubia laurae
Scutellaria sibthorpii
Sedum porphyreum
Teucrium divaricatum - ssp. canescens
Teucrium micropodioides

4. REGION OF KARPASSIA

Local endemics

....

Endemic to Cyprus

Anthemis tricolor
Asperula cypria
Astragalus cyprius
Bosea cypria
Dianthus cyprius
Dianthus strictus - var. troodi

Shown in black on the map opposite are the regions of Cyprus regarded as "bot-anical paradises", where most of the endemic species are concentrated

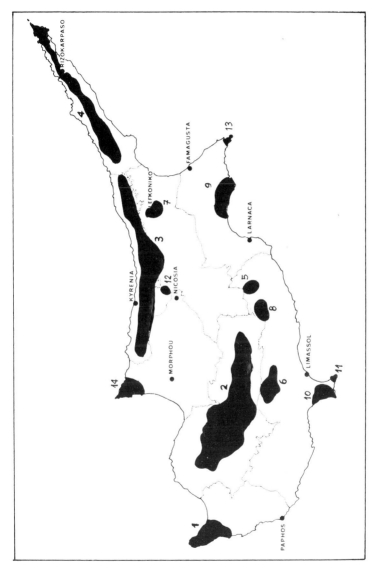

RIZOKARPASO

FAMAGUSTA

LEFKONIKO

LARNACA

KYRENIA

NICOSIA

MORPHOU

LIMASSOL

PAPHOS

4

13

7

9

3

12

5

8

2

6

10

11

14

1

Gagea juliae
Gladiolus triphyllus
Helianthemum obtusifolium
Limonium albidum - ssp. cyprium
Onobrychis venosa
Onosma fruticosum
Ophrys kotschyi
Origanum majorana - var. tenuifolium
Pimpinella cypria
Ptilostemon chamaepeuce - var. cyprius
Ranunculus millefoliatus - ssp. leptaleus
Scutellaria sibthorpii
Sedum porphyreum
Teucrium divaricatum - ssp. canescens
Teucrium micropodioides

5. REGION OF STAVROVOUNI

Local endemics

....

Endemic to Cyprus
Anthemis plutonia
Centranthus calcitrapa - ssp. orbiculatus
Gagea juliae
Gladiolus triphyllus
Onosma fruticosum
Phlomis brevibracteata
Scutellaria cypria - var. elatior
Thymus integer

6. REGION OF PERAPEDÍ - LOUVARAS - ZOOPIGÍ - KELAKI

Local endemics

....

Endemic to Cyprus

Acinos exiguus
Alyssum chondrogynum
Anthemis tricolor
Ballota integrifolia
Centaurea veneris
Hypericum repens
Origanum majorana - var. tenuifolium
Orobanche cypria
Pterocephalus multiflorus - ssp. multiflorus
Rubia laurae
Scabiosa cyprica
Scorzonera troodea

7. REGION OF LEFKÓNIKO - MILIA - PERISTERÓNA

Local endemics

....

Endemic to Cyprus
Centaurea calcitrapa - ssp. angusticeps
Hypericum repens
Onopordon cyprium
Sedum porphyreum

8. REGION OF LÉFKARA

Local endemics
Astragalus macrocarpus - ssp. lefkarensis

Endemic to Cyprus
Allium willeanum
Asperula cypria
Pterocephalus multiflorus - ssp. multiflorus
Ptilostemon chamaepeuce - var. cyprius
Scutellaria cypria - var. elatior
Teucrium micropodioides

9. REGION OF DEKÉLIA

Local endemics............................

Lara beach, in the region of Akamas.

Endemic to Cyprus

Anthemis tricolor
Astragalus cyprius
Carlina pygmaea

10. REGION OF AKROTÍRI - EPISKOPÍ

Local endemics

....

Endemic to Cyprus

Anthemis tricolor
Carlina pygmaea
Gladiolus triphyllus
Odontites cypria
Onosma fruticosa

Pterocephalus multiflorus - ssp. obtusifolius
Teucrium micropodioides

11. CAPE GATA

Local endemics
Convolvulus cyprius

Endemic to Cyprus
Anthemis tricolor
Odontites cypria

12. REGION OF MIÁ MILIÁ

Local endemics

....

Endemic to Cyprus
Anthemis tricolor
Carlina involucrata - var. cyprica
Carlina pygmaea

13. REGION OF CAVO GRECO

Local endemics

....

Endemic to Cyprus
Allium willeanum
Teucrium micropodioides

14. REGION OF KORMAKITIS - AGÍA IRÍNI

Local endemics

....

Endemic to Cyprus

Ophrys kotschyi
Senecio glaucus - ssp. cyprius
Teucrium micropodioides
Tulipa cypria

The above lists make it apparent that the most important habitat for rare plants endemic to Cyprus is the Troodos Range, where 44 local endemics and 36 plants endemic to Cyprus grow. The botanical paradise next in importance is the Pendadahtilos Range together with the region of Kyrenia and Kythrea, where 15 local endemics and 35 Cyprus endemics grow. Next is the Akamas Peninsula with one local endemic and 28 endemic to Cyprus, and the Karpassia Peninsula with no local endemics but 21 plants endemic to Cyprus.

The remaining ten regions have much smaller concentrations of endemics. Some endemic species, however, such as Tulipa cypria and Convolvulus cyprius are seriously threatened with extinction. Therefore the protection of certain of these habitats is of equal importance with the protection of Troodos, Akamas and Pendadahtilos.

LIST OF PLANTS ENDEMIC TO CYPRUS

1. Cedrus libani - ssp. brevifolia.
   Western Troodos Range, Tripilos Peak, Kilada ton Kédron.
2. Ranunculus cadmicus - var. cyprius
   Highest zone of the Troodos Range.
3. Ranunculus kykkoënsis
   Kiko Monastery, Kikkokampos road, south of Selac tou Pétrou.
4. Ranunculus millefoliatus - ssp. leptaleus
   Region of Kyrenia, lower slopes of Pendadahtilos Range, region of Limassol, Larnaca - Ormídia, Píri, Mia Milia, Nicosia, Karpassia, Apostolos Andreas.
5. Delphinium caseyi
   Pendadahtilos Range - peak southwest of Ágios Ilaríon Castle, Kiparissovouno.
6. Papaver argemone - ssp. meiklii
   Troodos Range: Platres, Kato Platres, Mandria

7. Brassica hilarionis
   Pendadahtilos Range, from Kornos to Giaila.
8. Thlaspi cyprium
   High peaks of the Troodos Range.
9. Alyssum troodi
   Troodos Range, Hionistra Peak and the village of Pródromos.
10. Alyssum chondrogynum
    Southern Cyprus, above Gerassa, between Pareklissa and Kelaki, above Panagia Glóssa and Kakomalis, near Louvaras.
11. Alyssum akamasicum
    Serpentine formations in the region of Akamas.
12. Arabis cypria
    Pendadahtilos Range and Karpassia.
13. Arabis purpurea
    Troodos Range, common.
14. Arabis kennedyae
    Troodos Range, Kríos Potamós and surrounding area. There is also an old reference to this species from Buffavento in the Pendadahtilos Range, probably erroneous.
15. Helianthemum obtusifolium
    Near the Pendadahtilos Range and in Kyrenia. Also in Akamas. Less common in the rest of Cyprus. Absent only from the Troodos Range.
16. Dianthus strictus - var. troodi
    Troodos Range, Agios Neófitos near Paphos, region of Larnaca, between Nicosia and Famagusta, Athalassa, Pendadahtilos Range, Karpassia peninsula.
17. Dianthus cyprius
    Pendadahtilos Range: Kornos, Agios Ilarion, Haléfka, etc. Karpassia: Koróvia.
18. Petrorhagia kennedyae
    Troodos Range. Also in Kokorantzia, between Nicosia and Limassol.
19. Saponaria cypria

49

Troodos Range, common.
20. Silene galataea
Troodos Range: Stavrós tis Psókas, Vroïssa, Tripilos, Prodromos and Galata.
21. Silene fraudatrix
Pendadahtilos Range: Halefka, Hartza, Antifonítis, Akanthoú.
22. Silene gemmata
Troodos Range, Platres, Mandria, Perapedí. Possibly also in Kyrenia.
23. Silene laevigata
Troodos Range: Platres, Zoopigí, Palehóri, Kambos. There is an old reference to this species from the region of Larnaca.
24. Arenaria rhodia - ssp. cypria
Troodos Range. Akamas: between Smigiés and Droússa. Agia Nikóla, above Neohorió. Karavópetres, near Lara.
25. Minuartia sintenisii
Troodos Range: Prodromos, Hionistra, Troodos, Livadia, Papoútsa.
26. Minuartia subtilis - ssp. filicaulis
Troodos Range: Hionístra, Troodos, Platania.
27. Hypericum repens
Troodos Range: Krios Potamos, Platres. Region of Limassol: Trimiklíni, Kakomalis. Region of Lefkóniko: Mia Milia, Kyrenia, Kythrea.
28. Genista sphacelata - var. crudelis
Troodos Range: Middle and upper zone.
29. Trifolium pamphylicum - var. dolichodontium
Troodos Range: Platres, Saïtas. Eastern Cyprus: Agios Mémnon.
30. Trifolium campestre - ssp. paphium
Troodos Range: Horterí Peak, above Stavros tis Psokas.
31. Astragalus suberosus - var. hartmannii
West of Nicosia.
32. Astragalus macrocarpus - ssp. lefkarensis
Kimolía Hill, above Pano Léfkara, on the path towards Kato Dri.
Very rare.

In the western part of the Troodos Range, a mixed forest of Cedar, Pine (Pinus brutia) and Cyprus oak (Quercus alnifolia).

34. Astragalus cyprius
    Akamas: Between the Agios Neofitos Monastery and Stefani.
    Troodos Range: Maheras Monastery, Hrisorogiatissa. East
    ern Cyprus: Between Cape Píla and Ormidia. Also common
    in the regions of Kyrenia, Karpassia and east of Nicosia.

35. Hedysarum cyprium
    Pendadahtilos Range. East of Nicosia: Hills between Latsia
    and Tséri.

36. Onobrychis venosa
    Akamas: Droussa. Statos (Paphos). Region of Limassol.
    Region of Larnaca. Region of Nicosia. Common in the Kyre-
    nia Range. Karpassia.

37. Rosa chionistrae
    Troodos Range: common in upper zone.

38. Rosularia cypria
Pendadahtilos Range: Agios Ilarion, Kyrenia, Buffavento, Giaila, Lapithos, Pendadahtilos.

39. Rosularia pallidiflora
Pendadahtilos Range: Agios Ilarion, Giaila, Belapassis, Pendadahtilos.

40. Sedum lampusae
Pendadahtilos Range. Common.

41. Sedum microstachyum
Troodos Range: Hionistra Peak.

42. Sedum cyprium
Akamas: Smigies Forest Station, Agia Nikola, above Neohorio. Troodos Range: Quite common in places.

43. Sedum porphyreum
Pendadahtilos Range: Quite common. Akamas: Stroúmbi, Droussa, Agia Nikola. Region of Limassol: Four miles north of Kandoú. Region of Larnaca: Sotíras, Agía Napa, Region east of Nicosia: Vatíli, Milia, Pigí. Karpassia: Agios Theodoros, near Rizokarpasso and Cape Andreas.

44. Bupleurum sintenisii
Region of Larnaca - Famagusta: Pérgamos, Troúli, Agios Geórgios. East of Nicosia: Between Nicosia and Kythrea, Athalassa, Limbia, near the Arhangelos Monastery.

45. Pimpinella cypria
Pendadahtilos Range: Very common. Karpassia: Near Kómi Kembír.

46. Ferulago cypria
Region of Kyrenia - Pendadahtilos Range: Between Kyrenia and Pano Díkomos, Agios Ilarion, Lefkoniko Pass.

47. Rubia laurae
Akamas: Lissós. Troodos Range: Platres, Afamís, Stavros tis Psokas, Messapotamós, Perapedi, Armínou. Region of Limassol: Marí, Kakomalis, above Louvaras. Pendadahtilos Range: Giaila, Halefka, Pendadahtilos, Kyrenia.

48. Asperula cypria
Common throughout Cyprus. Stroumbi, near Paphos. Troodos Range: Gialia, Kiko, Kakopetria, Agia Valley, Níkos.

A forest of Calabrian pine (Pinus brutia) in Akamas. In the foreground are a few Carob trees (Ceratonia siliqua).

Southern Cyprus: Kofinoú, Lefkara, Episkopi forest near Souni. Region of Larnaca - Famagusta: Between Foúrni and Athiénou. East of Nicosia: Athalassa. Pendadahtilos Range - Kyrenia: AboveKythrea, between Lefkoniko and Akanthou, Kyrenia, Armenion Monastery, Kandara etc. Karpassia: Komi Kembir.

49. Centranthus calcitrapa - ssp. orbiculatus
    Troodos Range: Near Finí, above Léfka, Kiko Monastery, Papoútsa, above Palehori, Agia Irini near Platres, Prodromos, Agia Valley, Paphos forest, Maheras Monastery (found by the author). Region of Limassol: Stavrovouni Monastery. Kyrenia: Andifonitis, Belapais, Armenian Monastery, Agios Ilaríon, Tripa Vouno.

50. Scabiosa cyprica
    Troodos Range: Perapedi, between Platres and Fini, Man-

dria, Ómodos, Kato Platres, Kilada Platí (found by the author). Region of Limassol: Dasos Oritaon, below Trimiklini, between Trimiklini and Perapedi, between Kivídes and Ezími.

51. Pterocephalus multiflorus - ssp. multiflorus
Troodos Range: Prodromos, Troodos, Platania, Platres, Seladi tou Pétrou. Region of Limassol: Trimiklini, Lefkara, Kakohorió.

52. Pterocephalus multiflorus - ssp. obtusifolius
Pendadahtilos Range: Common in many places. Region of Limassol: Dasos Akrotiríou. Morphou region: Agia Irini.

53. Anthemis tricolor
Akamas: Droussa. South of Paphos. Troodos Range: Near Gialia, Perapedi, Palehori, Pano Panagia. Region of Limassol: Between Nísou and Stavrovouni, Akrotiri, Skarinoú, Gerassa, Cape Gata, near Limassol. Region of Larnaca: Dekelia. Region of Famagusta, Nicosia, Kythrea, Mia Milia, Agios Varnavas Monastery, south of Koutsovéndis, Makedonítissa Monastery. Nicosia: Metóhi Kíkou. Region of Kyrenia - Pendadahtilos: Mountains above Kythrea, Agios Hrissóstomos Monastery, Kyrenia, Panagra, between Kythrea and Giaila, Larnaka tis Lapíthous, Dasos Lakovounaras, Karpassia.

54. Anthemis plutonia
Troodos Range: Prodromos, Hionistra, Krios Potamos, Xerokólimbos, Platres, Platania, Pedoulas, Papoutsa, Palehori, Maheras, Stavros tis Psokas. Region of Limassol: Agía Varvara (Stavrovouni).

55. Senecio glaucus - ssp. cyprius
Akamas: Karavópetres, near Agios Georgios, Agios Georgios islet. Paphos. Region of Morphou: Agia Irini, Kilada Xeroú.

56. Carlina involucrata - ssp. cyprica
Around Paphos. Akamas: Between Kouklia and Geroskípos. Troodos Range: Between Pano Platres and Perapedi, Vaza near Omodos, Perapedi, Prodromos. Region of Limassol: Eftagonia.
Eastern Cyprus: Agia Napa, Famagusta, Kythrea, Mia Milia, Limnia. Nicosia. Kyrenia.

57. Carlina pygmaea

Arabis purpurea, one of the most beautiful endemic plants of Cyprus.

Akamas: Smigies and areas of serpentine around Smigies. Troodos Range: Above Illías bridge, between Mesapotamos and Kato Amíandos, Kilada Routhkia, Troodos. Region of Limassol: Akrotiri, near Eftagonia. Region of Larnaca: Dekelia. East of Nicosia: Koutsovendis, between Vounó and Mia Milia. Kythrea, Vouno. Between Nicosia and Agírda.

58. Ptilostemon chamaepeuce - var. cyprius
    Akamas: Agios Neofitos, Gioulou near Loutra tis Afrodítis. Troodos Range: Near Galata, Prodromos, Kakopetria, Vouní, near Maheras Monastery, Troodos, Stavros tis Psokas. Region of Limassol: Between Limassol and Silikoú, Kalavassós, Lefkara, between Moní and Kelaki, Halassa. Pendadahtilos Range: Buffavento, Pendadahtilos, Kyrenia, Agios Ilarion, Kyrenia Pass, Koronia, Halefka, Karmí, Sina Oros. Karpassia: Near Komi Kembir.

59. Jurinea cypria

Troodos Range: Spilia, Hrisorogiatissa, Handria, Agrós, Troodos, Platres, Platania, Afamis, Perapedi.

60. Onopordon cyprium
Akamas: Cape Arnaoúti. Troodos Range: Krios Potamos, near Pedoulas, Evrihoú. Larnaca. East of Nicosia: Athalassa, road from Nicosia to Famagusta, around Nicosia. Above Peristerona. Region of Kyrenia: Near Kefalovrisso, Kythrea, between Belapais and Kyrenia, Kyrenia.

61. Centaurea veneris
Akamas: On serpentine on central ridge above Smigies. Region of Limassol: Dasos Lemessou, Kakomalis above Louvaras.

62. Centaurea calcitrapa - ssp. angusticeps
Around Kyrenia. Region of Morphou: Near Peristerona, Gerólakos. Nicosia. Kythrea. Between Prastió and Kouklia.

63. Taraxacum aphrogenes
Akamas: Agios Nikólaos. Also southeast of Paphos.

64. Taraxacum holmboei
Troodos Range: Platania, Prodromos, region of Hionistra.

65. Cephalorrhynchus cypricus
Troodos Range: Hionistra, Troodos, Krios Potamos, Xerokolimbos, Hartsís, Tripilos, Agios Theodoros River, near Stavros tis Psokas.

66. Scariola tetrantha
Troodos Range: Hionistra, Krios Potamos.

67. Scariola viminea (local form)
Troodos Range: Hionistra, Krios Potamos, Xerokolimbos.

68. Scorzonera troodea
Troodos Range: Hionistra, Platres, Prodromos, Omodos, Agios Nikolaos etc. Region of Limassol: Kakomalis, above Louvaras.

69. Limonium albidum - ssp. cyprium
Region of Kyrenia: Near Panagia i Glikiótissa Church and east of Kyrenia. Karpassia: Cape Andreas.

70. Cyclamen cyprium
Akamas: Toxeftra, near Agios Georgios, Smigies. Troodos Range: Galata, Evrihou, Perapedi, Platres, Vroissa, Lagou-

Scene with Pines and shrubs in the Akamas peninsula: a typical Mediterranean ecosystem which has not yet been strongly influenced by man.

dera, Kilada tou Pírgou, Kalopanagiótis, Kiko, Stavros tis Psokas, Nikos, etc. Pendadahtilos Range: Agioś Ilarion, Kyrenia, Agios Amvróssios, Karmi, Vassília, Belapais, Kazani, Sísklipos, Pendadahtilos.

71. Cynoglossum troodi
Troodos Range: Troodos, Krios Potamos, Xerokolimbos, Hionistra.

72. Onosma fruticosum
Akamas: Smigies, Psíndro near Agios Georgios. Region of Troodos: Afamis, road to Maheras. Region of Limassol: Stavrovouni, Kofinou, Episkopi, Dasos Oritaon, Amathoús, Limassol. Eastern Cyprus: Athalassa, near Famagusta, Ormidia, Gossí. Region of Morphou: Agia Irini, between Mirtou and Cape Kormakitis. Region of Kyrenia: Kandara, Kyrenia, Pendadahtilos, Akanthou, Kornos, etc. Karpassia: Cape

Andreas, between Gialoússa and Agios Andrónikos, Kóma tou Gialoú.

73. Onosma troodi
Troodos Range: Hionistra, Krios Potamos, around Platres, Papoutsa.

74. Onosma caespitosum
Pendadahtilos Range: Buffavento, Pendadahtilos, Agios Ilarion, Lapithos, Larnaka tis Lapithou, Giaila, Kornos, etc.

75. Convolvulus x cyprius
Region of Limassol: Cape Gata.

76. Od   ontites cypria
Western Cyprus: Agios Neofitos Monastery. Troodos Range: Prodromos, Fini, Platres, Galata, Trikoukia, Kalopanagiotis, etc. Region of Limassol: Cape Gata, Episkopi. East of Nicosia: Kythrea. Pendadahtilos Range: Agios Ilarion, Giaila, near Mirtou, Kyrenia pass.

77. Orobanche cypria
Troodos Range: Prodromos, Platres, Hrissorogiatissa, Agios Nikolaos, Statos. Region of Limassol: Kalavassos, Kakomalis.

78. Origanum cordifolium
Troodos Range: Kilada Routhkia, Kilada Palehoríou, Kilada Stenoús, Kilada Alonoúdi, Kilada Xerou (found by the author).

79. Origanum syriacum - var. bevanii
Kyrenia: Near Lapithos.

80. Origanum majorana - var. tenuifolium
Akamas: Lissos, between Pólis and Stroumbi, Kakóskala. Region of Troodos: Afamis. Region of Limassol: Near Trimik lini. Region of Kyrenia: Mirtou, Pendadahtilos, Agios Ilarion, Agios Epíktitos, Agios Amvrossios, Koronia, Ardana, Buffavento, Halefka, Giaila, Mandres, Mersiníki, Lapithos, Kyrenia. Karpassia: Apostolos Andreas, Ambéli, Afendrika, Kandara Castle, Gióti, Goniés, Peristergiés, Gialoússa.

81. Thymus integer
Akamas: Karavopetres near Agios Georgios, Mélanos near

Anthemis plutonia, a typical Cyprus endemic which grows on volcanic soil.

Agios Georgios, between Ínia and Smigies. Troodos Range: Evrihou, Hrissorogiatissa, Troodítissa, Stavros tis Psokas, Platania, Platres, Vavatsinia, Filégia above Pírgos, between Prodromos and Agios Nikolaos, Hionistra, Pedoulas. Region of Limassol: Stavrovouni, near Apsioú, near Mosfilóti, Kofinou.

82. Micromeria chionistrae
Troodos Range: Kiko Monastery, Krios Potamos, Xerokolimbos, Hionistra, Fini, above Stavros tis Psokas, above Prodromos, above Trooditissa.

83. Acinos exiguus
Troodos Range: Near Fini, Hionistra Peak, between Platres and Troodos, Xerokolimbos, Krios Potamos, east of Hionistra, Livadi tou Pasha, Troodos, near Prodromos, Tripilos, near Kakopetria. Region of Limassol: Kakomalis above Louvaras.

84. Acinos troodi
    Troodos Range: Hionistra, Moní tou Peloú, Troodos near Government House.
85. Salvia willeana
    Troodos Range: Hionistra, Trooditissa, Prodromos, Pedoulas, Platres, Troodos, Amiandos, etc.
86. Salvia veneris
    Eastern Cyprus: On marl, sandstone hummocks and lava intrusions around Kythrea and Kefalovrisso.
87. Nepeta troodi
    Troodos Range: Hionistra Peak, Krios Potamos, Xerokolimbos, Moniatis, Kiko, Madarí, Papoutsa, south of Trikoukia.
88. Sideritis cypria
    Pendadahtilos Range: Buffavento, Pendadahtilos, Agios Ilarion, Halefka, Belapais, above Kythrea, above Sisklipos.
89. Ballota integrifolia
    Akamas: Lissos, above Pégia, Ktíma. Paphos. Region of Troodos: Vouni Palace. Region of Limassol: Lania, between Limassol and Trimiklini, Arminou, between Ahélia and Pissoúri. Pendadahtilos Range: Kyrenia Pass, between Buffavento and Agios Hrissostomos Monastery, near Pendadahtilos, Panagia Plataniótissa, southern slopes of Buffavento.
90. Phlomis cypria - var. cypria
    Pendadahtilos Range: Agios Ilarion and Karavas.
91. Phlomis cypria - var. occidentalis
    Akamas: Mavrohómata, between Lissos and Avdoulína. Troodos Range: Atratsa, Kilada Marathassas, Stavros tis Psokas, near Alonoúdi.
92. Phlomis brevibracteata
    Region of Limassol: Kakorantzia, between Trimiklini and Lania, Zagala above Trimiklini. Pendadahtilos Range: between Kandara and Davlós, near Kandara, Panagra gorge, Ardana, Akanthou.
93. Scutellaria sibthorpii
    Pendadahtilos Range - region of Kyrenia: Andifonitis, Pendadahtilos, Agios Hrissostomos Monastery, Kyrenia, Lapos, Kandara, Agios Ilarion, Koronia, above Kythrea, Halefka,

Gorge in the region of Akamas. At the mouth of the gorge are wild Cypresses.

Karavas, Kornos, Larnaka tis Lapithou. Karpassia. Livadia, Komi Kebir, Agios Theodoros.

94. Scutellaria cypria - var. cypria
Troodos Range: Hionistra, Platania, Platres, Xerokolimbos, Krios Potamos, Fini, Kiko, Stavros tis Psokas, Lemíthou, Amiandos, Prodromos, Agia, above Spilia, Kakopetria, etc.

95. Scutellaria cypria - var. elatior
Akamas: Tsanda, Stroumbi, Droussa. Troodos Range: Hrissorogiatissa, Platres, Kiko, Zoopigi, Perapedi. Region of Limassol: Fassoula, Lania, Lefkara, and near Apsiou.

96. Teucrium divaricatum - ssp. canescens
Troodos Range, region of Limassol, Eastern Cyprus, Karpassia and region of Kyrenia.

97. Teucrium cyprium - ssp. cyprium
Troodos Range: Hionistra, Platres, Krios Potamos, Kiko, between Ambelikoú and Kambos, Madarí, Alonoudi, Kilada

Agias, Troodos, Prodromos, etc.

98. Teucrium cyprium - ssp. kyreniae
Pendadahtilos Range: Buffavento, Giaila, Larnaka tis Lapithou, Agios Ilarion, etc.

99. Teucrium micropodioides
Akamas: Lissos, Mandria. Region of Limassol: Lefkara, near Akrotiri, near Limassol, Cape Zevgari. Region of Larnaca: Cavo Greco. East of Nicosia: Athalassa and between Nicosia and Famagusta. Region of Morphou: Between Morphou and Kormakitis, Agia Irini. Region of Kyrenia: Mountains above Kythrea, between Akanthou and Kyrenia, Pendadahtilos, Halefka, Ano Thermia, Karpassia: Near Komi Kebir, Agios Andronikos, near Agios Ilías.

100. Bosea cypria
Akamas: Droussa, Pegia. Paphos. Troodos: Lefka. Region of Limassol: Kalavassos. Region of Larnaca-Famagusta: Sotiras, Agios Andónios, near Famagusta, Larnaca, Nicosia, Agia Irini, Diório. Region of Kyrenia: Lapithos, Ahiropíitos, Kyrenia, Agios Epiktitos, Agios Amvrossios, Akanthou, Agios Ilarion. Halefka, Vassilia, Kazafani, etc. Karpassia: Eptahóri, Gialoussa, Akrades, Rizokarpasso.

101. Euphorbia cassia - ssp. rigoi
Troodos Range: Hionistra, Platres, Prodromos, Amiandos, etc.

102. Euphorbia veneris
Troodos Range: Prodromos, Troodos, Platres, Fini, Saitas, etc.

103. Quercus alnifolia
Troodos Range: Quite common in very many places.

104. Ophrys kotschyi
Region of Limassol: Ipsónas, Kofinou. West of Nicosia. Near Larnaca. Between Nicosia and Evlénia. Lapithos. Near Kormakiti. Region of Pendadahtilos-Kyrenia: Pendadahtilos, Olimbos, Mirtou, Klepíni, between Halefka and Hartza, Kyre-

Forest of Cedars and Pines in the western Troodos Range.

nia, above Agios Amvrossios. Karpassia: Agios Andronikos, Rónas Bay, Gialoussa.

105. **Orchis anatolica - var. troodi**
Troodos Range: Near Galata, Kakopetria, Saitas, Platania, Krios Potamos, Platres, Pirgos, Stavros tis Psokas, Prodromos, Kiko, Kilada Agias, Zaharou, etc. Also Stavrovouni.

106. **Crocus cyprius**
Troodos Range: Hionistra, around Troodos, Kanoúres Springs, Prodromos, Amiandos, below Platania.

107. **Crocus hartmannianus**
Troodos Range: Kiónia above Maheras Monastery. Pendadahtilos Range: Peak to the west of Tripa Vouno.

108. **Gladiolus triphyllus**
Akamas: Polis, Agios Georgios, Loutra tis Afroditis, Fontana Amorosa. Paphos. Troodos Range: Southern slopes, between Agia and Stavros tis Psokas, near Dódeka Anémi Pass, Tripilos, between Tripilos and Stavros tis Psokas, Kambos, Gialia, between Kiko and Pómos. Region of Limassol: Between Pissouri and Kouklia, Episkopi, Paramali, Kouklia, road from Kelaki to Limassol. Region of Kyrenia: Between Melandrína and Andifonitis, Kornos, above Larnaka tis Lapithou. Karpassia: Near Afendrika (Epiótissa), Agios Vakos near Gialoussa.

109. **Tulipa cypria**
Akamas: Kakoskala, above Agios Nikolaos, Region of Morphou: Kormakiti, Diorios. Region of Kyrenia: Mirtou, Agios Pandeleimon.

110. **Gagea juliae**
Akamas: Erimídes near Agios Georgios, Smigies. Troodos Range: Platres, Krios Potamos, Hionistra, Kionia, Vavatsinia, above Kakopetria, road to Maheras, above Klírou, Troodos, Stavros tis Psokas. Region of Limassol: Near Paramítha, Limassol-Nicosia road, above Kelaki, above Mosfiloti, north of Kofinou, between Kelaki and Pareklissa. Pendadahtilos Range: Pendadahtilos, Agios Ilarion, Kandara, Kiparissovouno, Kornos and near Kyrenia. Karpassia: Gialoussa.

111. **Allium cupanii - ssp. cyprium**

Euphorbia veneris

Athalassa. Between Potamí and Evrihou, Peristerona.

112. Allium autumnale
Troodos Range: East of Platres, Saitas. Region of Kyrenia: Near Mirtou, Vassilia, Akanthou, Karavas.

113. Allium paniculatum - ssp. exaltatum
Troodos Range: West of Asprokremnos on the southern slopes of Hionistra, Xerokolimbos, Krios Potamos, Platres.

114. Allium willeanum
Akamas: Near Agios Neofitos Monastery. Troodos Range: Between Prodromos and Galata, near Kaminaria, Kakopetria, Platres between Ambelikoú and Kambos, Kambos. Region of Limassol: Lefkara. Region of Famagusta: Cavo Greco. Region of Morphou: Órga. Region of Kyrenia: Agios Ilarion, Buffavento, Kyrenia, Belapais, Lapithos, Halefka, near Panagra.

115. Ornithogalum chionophilum

Kipriakó díktamo (Origanum cordifolium), one of the rarest endemic plants of Cyprus.

      Troodos Range: Hionistra, Tripilos, Palehori, Lagoudera, Prodromos, Krios Potamos, Moniatis, Xerokolimbos, etc.
116. Scilla morrisii
      Troodos Range: Near the Hrissorogiatissa Monastery.
117. Chionodoxa lochiae
      Troodos Range: Near Spilia, Pedoulas, Pródromos, Platania, etc.
118. Cyperus cyprius
    Troodos Range: Prodromos, near Poditoú-Monastery, Galata, Krios Potamos, Kilada Routhkia.
119. Lindbergella sintenisii
      Troodos Range: Prodromos, Hionistra, Messapotamos, Platres, Kakopetria, Pedoulas, etc.
120. Agrostis cypricola
      Region of Kyrenia: Kyrenia Pass (Bogazi) above Kyrenia.
121. Brachypodium firmifolium
      Troodos Range: Messapotamos, Krios Potamos, Livadi tou Pasha.

cream or creamy		dark green	
pale yellow		light green or grass-green	
lemon-yellow		glaucous	
golden-yellow		grey-green or greyish-green	
orange		silvery	
red		white	
crimson		pale pink	
blackish-red		pink	
dark brown		purple	
light brown		dark violet or mauve	
grey		violet	
blue		lilac	
dark or deep blue		pale blue	

Because in the text colours and hues of flowers or leaves alluded are difficult for the reader to comprehend fully, a list of colours and their names has been provided.

GLOSSARY

glandular 1

flower (sex)
  male 2
  bisexual
  or hermaphrodite 3
  female 4

ray floret 5
tubular or disk flroret 6
fusiform or spindle - shaped 7
apical 8

flowers (shape)
  actinomorphic 9
  zygomorphic 10
  butterfly-like
  or papilionaceous 11

anther 12
pedicel 13
arachnoid lanate 14
distant 15

stem (shape)
  quadrangular 16
  cylindrical 17
  hollow 18
  winged 19

stem (position)
  ascending 20
  creeping 21
  erect 22
  arcuate or arched 23

bract 24
bracteole 25
woody short-shoot 26
cluster 27
dioecious 28 ★
terminal 29
sessile or stalkless 8b
blade or lamina 8c
petiolate 32
caducous or falling early 33
depressed (hairs
  or other parts) 34
papillose or warty 34b
catkin 35
calyx 10b

fruit (type)
  achene 6b
  drupe 38
  carpel 39
  nut 40

★   28. Having male and female flowers on different plants

68

capsule 41
siliqua or silicula 42
pod 43
berry 44
samara 45
legume or pod 46
legume articulate or jointed 47
legume constricted 48

sheath 49
tuber 50
cup or cupule 51
decurved 52
deflexed 53
incurved 54
recurved 55
reflexed 56
scale 5b
hairless or glabrous 58
lobe 59
lanate 60
axil - axillary 61
leaf - stolk or petiole 62
solitary 63
monoecious 64 ★
vein 65
filament 12b
claw 67
corona 68
stipules 69
perianth 70
perianth segment 71
spur 72
wing 19b
pyramidal crown 74
peak 75
rhizome 76
rosette 77
clavate or club-shaped 78
spathe 79

corolla or calyx
    two-lipped 10c
    bell-shaped or campanulate 52
    cup-shaped or crateriform 81
    tubular 82
    rotate or wheel-shaped 83
    funnel-shaped 84

stamen 12c
stolon 86
tube 87

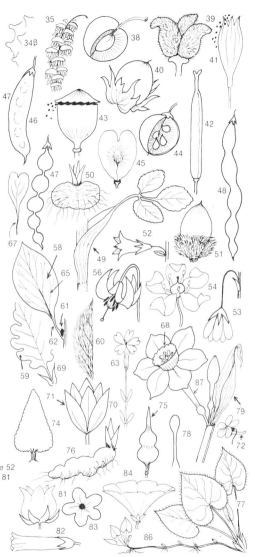

64. Having male and female flowers in the same plant

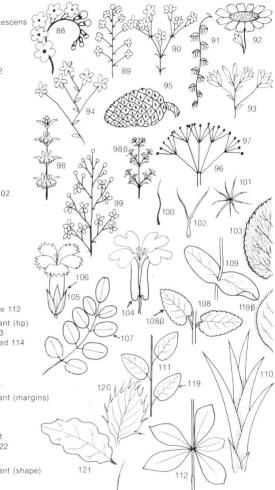

inflorescence or infructescens
   curl 88
   raceme 89
   dichasium 90
   catkin 91
   head or capitulum 92
   corymb 93
   cyme or cymose 94
   cone 95
   umbel 96
   secondary umbel 97
   spike 98
   spikelet 98 b
   panicle 99

hairs (shape)
   simple 100
   star-shaped 101
   forked or bifurcate 102

hairy 103
saccate 104
epicalyx 105
epicalyx scales 106
leaflet 107

leaves (position)
   opposite 108
   perforate 109
   distichous 110
   alternate 111
   whorled or verticillate 112

leaf or other part of plant (tip)
   aristate or awned 113
   emarginate or notched 114
   obtuse 115
   mucronate 116
   truncate 117
   acute 118

leaf or other part of plant (margins)
   entire 119
   ciliate 119b
   fimbriate 120
   undulate or wavy 121
   dentate or toothed 122
   crenate 108b

leaf or other part of plant (shape)
   obcordate 124
   oblanceolate 125
   obovate 126
   shield - like or peltate 127
   canaliculate or chanelled 128
   sagittal or arrow - shaped 129
   needle 130

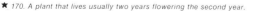

★ 170. A plant that lives usually two years flowering the second year.   ★ 171. A plant that lives

70

decurrent 131
bractlike 132
lingulate
   or tongue - shaped 133
linear 134
deltoid 135
bilobed 136
orbicular 137
bipinnately lobed 138
bipinnate 139
bifid or bipartite 140
bifurcate 141
elliptical 142
semitubular 143
cordate
   or heart - shaped 144
lanceolate
   or lance - shaped 145
lyrate 146
reniform
   or kidney - shaped 147
filiform 148
subulate
   or awl - shaped 149
palmately - lobed 150
palmatifid or palmate 151
amplexicaul
   or stem - clasping 152
pedate 153
oblong 154
pinnately - lobed 155
pinnate or pinnatifid 107
rhomboidal 156
gladiate or sword - shaped 110
spathulate 159
cuneate 160
tubular 161
strap - shaped 162
trifoliate 163
ovate or egg - shaped 164
plant (shape)
   tree 74
   shrub 166
   cushion - shaped
   shrublet 168 or pulvinate 167
   caespitose 169
plant (duration of life)
   biennial 170 ★
   annual 171 ★
   perennial 172 ★
pubescent or downy 173
ovary (position)
   superior 174
   semi-inferior 175
   inferior 176
auricle 177
only one year or less.   ★ 172. A plant whose underground parts, at least, live for several years.

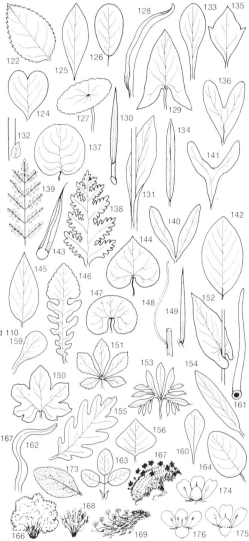

71

KEY TO FAMILIES

Plants without flowers or seed ....111.
   Pteridophyta
Plants with flowers and seeds:
   Plants without chlorophyll, variously coloured, but
   not green, parasites and saprophytes.. **GROUP A**
   Plants green, with chlorophyll:
     Flowers crowded into heads surrounded by an
     involucre .... **GROUP B**
     Flowers not crowded into involucrate heads:
       Leaves reduced to small scales or absent............................. **GROUP C**
       Leaves (or apparent leaves) with a distinct
       lamina:
         Trees, shrubs and woody climbers:
           Leaves opposite or whorled .... **GROUP D**
           Leaves alternate or irregularly inserted........................ **GROUP E**
         Herbs:
           Leaves opposite or whorled .... **GROUP F**
         Leaves alternate or all basal:
           Leaves compound or deeply divided........................ **GROUP G**
           Leaves simple.. **GROUP H**

GROUP A

PLANTS WITHOUT CHLOROPHYLL, VARIOUSLY COLOURED BUT NOT
GREEN: PARASITES AND SAPROPHYTES
Trailing or climbing plants with thread - like
stems .... 65. Convolvulaceae
Erect herbs:
   Flowers in sessile or subsessile clusters;
   plant without any obvious stem .... 77. Rafflesiaceae
   Flowers in stalked spikes or racemes:
     Flowers actinomorphic; corolla polype-
     talous; ovary superior... 56. Monotropaceae
     Flowers zygomorphic:
       Ovary superior; corolla tubular............................ 68. Orobanchaceae
       Ovary inferior; corolla of free petals.................... 93. Orchidaceae

GROUP B

FLOWERS CROWDED INTO HEADS SURROUNDED BY AN INVOLUCRE
Petals free:
   Leaves opposite, simple.. 16. Caryophyllaceae
   Leaves alternate, generally compound or
   deeply lobed:
     Ovary superior .... 33. Leguminosae

Landscape in the Akamas peninsula

Ovary inferior.. 45. Umbelliferae

Petals united into a tubular or ligulate
corolla:

    Anthers united into a tube around the
    style .... 53. Compositae

    Anthers free:

        Leaves in whorls .... 49. Rubiaceae

        Leaves not in whorls:

            Ovary superior..................................... 71. Labiatae

            Ovary inferior...................................... 52. Dipsacaceae

GROUP C

LEAVES REDUCED TO SMALL SCALES OR ABSENT

Leaves reduced to small scales adpressed to
stems:

    Flowers with a coloured perianth:

        Perianth pink or pinkish .... 19. Tamaricaceae

        Perianth yellow .... 80. Thymelaeaceae

    Flowers without a perianth .... 2. Cupressaceae

Leaves absent:

    Stems articulated:

        Flowers with a conspicuous, coloured
        corolla... 43a. Cactaceae

        Flowers inconspicuous, without a corolla:

            Stems succulent .... 74. Chenopodiaceae

            Stems not succulent:

                Fruit fleshy; shrubs and woody
                climbers .... 3. Ephedraceae

                Fruit not fleshy, cone-like; tall shrubs
                and trees................................. 88a. Casuarinaceae

    Stems not articulated:

        Stems branched, often climbing or
        sprawling.. 97. Liliaceae

        Stems not branched, erect....................... 98. Juncaceae

GROUP D

TREES, SHRUBS AND WOODY CLIMBERS WITH UNIFORMLY OPPOSITE OR WHORLED LEAVES

Flowers inconspicuous, without any obvious
perianth or coloured bracts:

    Leaves simple:

        Leaves subulate or scale-like .... 2. Cupressaceae

        Leaves oblong-elliptic....................................... 74. Chenopodiaceae

    Leaves imparipinnate .... 60. Oleaceae

Flowers with a coloured perianth or corolla,
or conspicuous coloured bracts:

    Bracts conspicuous, coloured; perianth
    inconspicuous ....72a. Nyctaginaceae

Bracts inconspicuous; perianth or corolla
conspicuous:
  Petals (or coloured sepals) free:
    Stamens very numerous:
      Woody climbers, leaves with twisting
      petioles .... 4. Ranunculaceae
      Erect shrubs or trees; petioles not
      twisting:
        Leaves gland-dotted:
          Petals yellow .... 21. Guttiferae
          Petals not yellow .... 39. Myrtaceae
        Leaves not gland-dotted:
          Sepals red, fleshy, persistent .... 40a. Punicaceae
          Sepals not red or fleshy .... 12. Cistaceae
    Stamens 10 or fewer:
      Leaves fleshy .... 25. Zygophyllaceae
      Leaves not fleshy:
        Sepals united into a tube.................................. 16. Caryophyllaceae
        Sepals free .... 3. Aceraceae
  Petals united:
    Ovary inferior:
      Leaves imparipinnate.. 48. Sambucaceae
      Leaves simple or irregularly lobed:
        Leaves exstipulate, opposite;
        flowers zygomorphic .... 47. Caprifoliaceae
        Leaves stipulate, opposite or appa-
        rently whorled; flowers actinomor-
        phic.. 49. Rubiaceae
    Ovary superior:
      Stamens 2:
        Flowers actinomorphic .... 60. Oleaceae
        Flowers zygomorphic .... 71. Labiatae
      Stamens 4-10:
        Leaves compound:
          Leaves palmately compound .... 70. Verbenaceae
          Leaves pinnately compound .... 69a. Bignoniaceae
        Leaves simple:
          Flowers actinomorphic:
            Stamens 8-10, twice as many
            as corolla-lobes... 55. Ericaceae
            Stamens 4-5, as many as corol-
            la-lobes:
              Leaves toothed .... 62a. Loganiaceae
            Leaves entire:
               Corolla with a central corona .... 62. Asclepiadaceae
              Corolla without a central
              corona... 61. Apocynaceae

Flowers zygomorphic:
    Style gynobasic; fruit a nutlet .... 71. Labiatae
    Style terminal:
        Fruit fleshy, drupaceous .... 70. Verbenaceae
        Fruit a capsule or follicle:
            Inflorescence spicate, conspi-
            cuously bracteate; seeds not
            winged.. 69c. Acanthaceae
            Inflorescence paniculate, not
            conspicuously bracteate;
            seeds winged:
                Corolla white, blotched
                yellow, fruit linear, very
                elongate and narrow .... 69a. Bignoniaceae
                Corolla blue or mauve; fruit
                an ovoid, woody capsule.. ..... 67. Scrophulariaceae

GROUP E

HERBS WITH OPPOSITE OR WHORLED LEAVES
Leaves compound or lobed almost to base:
  Petals free:
    Flowers zygomorphic, spurred...................................... 8. Fumariaceae
    Flowers actinomorphic, not spurred:
        Fruit beaked .... 26. Geraniaceae
        Fruit not beaked .... 25. Zygophyllaceae
  Petals united into a tube:
    Inflorescence a spike .... 70. Verbenaceae
    Inflorescence a cyme, corymb or umbel:
        Flowers zygomorphic, corolla-tube
        longer than limb.. 51. Valerianaceae
        Flowers actinomorphic, subrotate, co-
        rolla-tube shorter than limb .... 48. Sambucaceae
Leaves simple:
  Flowers without petals or coloured perianth:
    Aquatic herbs, floating or rooting in mud .... 38. Callitrichaceae
    Terrestrial herbs:
        Fruit a capsule:
            Fruit 2 (-3) - lobed, with 1 seed in each
            lobe.. 83. Euphorbiaceae
            Fruit without lobes, containing nume-
            rous small seeds:
                Ovary 1 - locular........................... 16. Caryophyllaceae
               Ovary 3-5 - locular......................... 44. Aizoaceae
Fruit an indehiscent nut, drupe or
        achene:
            Leaves linear, subulate or narrowly
            oblong, without a distinct lamina and

petiole.. 17. Illecebraceae
Leaves with a distinct lamina and
petiole:
   Leaves glabrous or subglabrous,
   somewhat fleshy... 50. Theligonaceae
   Leaves pubescent, strigose or
   hispid, not fleshy .... 54. Urticaceae
Flowers with petals or coloured perianth:
  Petals (or perianth-segments) free:
    Leaves dotted with translucent glands .... 21. Guttiferae
    Leaves not gland-dotted:
     Leaves fleshy... 36. Crassulaceae
     Leaves not fleshy:
      Sepals united into a tube:
       Style 1, simple .... 40. Lythraceae
       Styles 2 or more, free or connate
       towards base:
        Styles connate below .... 15. Frankeniaceae
        Styles free to base............................16. Caryophyllaceae
      Sepals not united into a tube:
       Style 1, simple; stamens usually
       numerous.. 12. Cistaceae
       Styles 2 or more, free or connate
       towards base:
        Flowers in cymes or pseudo-ra-
        cemes....................16. Caryophyllaceae
        Flowers solitary, axillary .... 20. Elatinaceae
  Petals (or perianth) united into a tube:
   Ovary inferior:
    Leaves in apparent whorls .... 49. Rubiaceae
    Leaves opposite.. 51. Valerianaceae
   Ovary superior or apparently superior:
    Corolla zygomorphic:
     Fruit a capsule:
      Capsule at least twice as long as
      wide .... 69b. Pedaliaceae
      Capsule not twice as long as wide   67. Scrophulariaceae
     Fruit a nutlet or berry:
      Ovary deeply 4-lobed; style
      usually gynobasic, corolla mostly
      strongly zygomorphic................................ 71. Labiatae
Ovary not, or shallowly 4-lobed;
      style terminal; corolla often weakly
      zygomorphic .... 70. Verbenaceae
    Corolla actinomorphic:
     Corolla-lobes asymmetric............................... 61. Apocynaceae
     Corolla-lobes symmetric or nearly so:

Fruit a capsule or follicle contain-
ing 2 or more seeds:
    Inflorescence a dense spike.................. 72. Plantaginaceae
    Inflorescence not a spike:
        Corolla with a central corona 62. Asclepiadaceae
        Corolla without a central co-
        rona:
            Fruit a follicle; seeds
            crowned with silky hairs .... 61. Apocynaceae
            Fruit a capsule;
                Stamens opposite co-
                rolla-lobes; flowers soli-
                tary, axillary.............................. 58. Primulaceae
                Stamens alternating with
                corolla-lobes; flowers in
                terminal cymes .... 63. Gentianaceae
            Fruit indehiscent, 1-seeded...... 72a. Nyctaginaceae

GROUP F
TREES, SHRUBS AND WOODY CLIMBERS WITH ALTERNATE OR IRREGULARLY
INSERTED LEAVES

Leaves needle-like:
  Fruit a woody cone; flowers without a
  perianth.. 1. Pinaceae
  Fruit not a woody cone; flowers with a
  perianth.. 79a. Proteaceae
Leaves not needle-like:
  Leaves compound or lobed almost to base:
    Woody climbers .... 30. Vitaceae
    Shrubs or trees:
      Leaves harsh, leathery or fibrous, crowd-
      ed at the apex of a bare trunk .... 98a. Palmae
      Leaves not as above:
        Leaves pleasantly or unpleasantly
        aromatic when crushed:
            Plant armed with prickles .... 34. Rosaceae
Plant unarmed:
            Shrub with glandular-punctate
            leaves .... 28. Rutaceae
            Tree; leaves not glandular-
            punctate.. 88. Juglandaceae
        Leaves not aromatic or malodorous
        when crushed:
            Leaves stipulate:
               Fruit a pod.. 33. Leguminosae
              Fruit indehiscent, fleshy or spongy................... 34. Rosaceae
            Leaves exstipulate:

Leaves pinnate
    Leaves with 13-40 leaflets:
        Leaflets ovate, toothed; fruit
        a samara ....   28a. Simaroubaceae
        Leaflets linear-lanceolate, en-
        tire or serrulate; fruit a drupe....................   32. Anacardiaceae
    Leaves with fewer than 13
    leaflets:
        Stamens with filaments united
        into a column; fruit a drupe ....   28b. Meliaceae
        Stamens free:
            Fruit an inflated capsule or
            large, fleshy, yellow or orange
            drupe ....   30a. Sapindaceae
            Fruit a small, brownish or red-
            dish resinous drupe ....   32. Anacardiaceae
    Leaves irregularly dissected, not
    pinnate ....   79a. Proteaceae
Leaves simple:
  Woody climbers:
    Stems prickly...   97. Liliaceae
    Stems not prickly:
      Leaves persistent, evergreen; plant
      without tendrils:
        Flowers solitary, axillary; perianth
        tubular..   78. Aristolochiaceae
        Flowers in umbels; perianth not
        tubular..   46. Araliaceae
      Leaves deciduous; plant with tendrils........................   30. Vitaceae
  Shrubs or trees:
    Flowers with distinct sepals and petals:
      Petals free:
        Ovary borne on a distinct stipe; fila-
        ments tinged mauve or pink....................................   10. Capparaceae
Ovary sessile or subsessile:
        Leaves clothed with stellate hairs:
          Stamens connate, forming a sta-
          minal column; epicalyx generally
          present..   22. Malvaceae
          Stamens not forming a staminal
          column; epicalyx absent ....   23. Tiliaceae
        Leaves with simple hairs or glabrous:
          Fruit a pod ....   33. Leguminosae
          Fruit fleshy or spongy, indehiscent:
            Flowers very small; petals often
            absent; stamens 4-5 ....   29. Rhamnaceae
            Flowers conspicuous; petals

well developed; stamens usually
numerous .... 34. Rosaceae
Petals united:
  Corolla-tube distinctly narrowed above:
    Flowers unisexual, solitary or in
    small axillary clusters .... 58a. Ebenacee
    Flowers hermaphrodite in branched
    terminal panicles .... 55. Ericaceae
  Corolla-tube cylindrical or widened
  towards apex:
    Inflorescence racemose .... 59. Styracaceae
    Inflorescence not racemose; flowers
    solitary or in cymes or clusters:
      Fruit a capsule or many-seeded
      berry .... 66. Solanaceae
      Fruit a 1-seeded drupe .... 64. Boraginaceae
Flowers apetalous or with an undifferentiat-
ed calyx and corolla:
  Leaves palmately lobed:
    Fruits crowded into pedunculate, glo-
    bose clusters:
    Base of petiole calyptrate; fruit im-
    mersed in a basal tuft of bristles .... 87. Platanaceae
    Base of petiole not calyptrate; fruit
    without a basal tuft of bristles 37.Hamamelidaceae
      Fruits not in pedunculate, globose
      clusters:
        Fruit fleshy, indehiscent .... 86. Moraceae
        Fruit a capsule .... 83. Euphorbiaceae
      Stamens very numerous,
      conspicuous .... 39. Myrtaceae
      Stamens few, inconspicuous .... 79. Lauraceae
  Leaves not aromatic when crushed:
    Fruit a fleshy berry, drupe or cluster
    of drupes:
      Leaves covered with silvery, flat
      scale-hairs .... 81. Elaeagnaceae
      Leaves not covered with scale-
      hairs:
        Branches spinose or prickly:
          Flowers bright yellow .... 6. Berberidaceae
          Flowers creamy-white .... 97. Liliaceae
        Branches not spinose or prickly:
          Leaves (or apparent leaves)
          rigid, pungent .... 97. Liliaceae
          Leaves not rigid or pungent:
            Fruit a cluster or drupelets

```
              or a syconium ...............................   86. Moraceae
          Fruit not as above:
              Perianth brightly coloured   *80. Thymelaeaceae
              Perianth greenish, incon-
              spicuous:
                  Fruit bright red or orange:
                      Leaves sparse, linear;
                      flowers in short axilla-
                      ry racemes .........................   82. Santalaceae
                      Leaves copious, broadly
                      lanceolate, ovate or
                      elliptic; flowers in ter-
                      minal spikes or pani-
                      cles.....................................   73. Amaranthaceae
                  Fruit dull greenish, brown-
                  ish or blackish:
                      Leaves coarsely
                      toothed or lobed ...............   85. Ulmaceae
                      Leaves shortly
                      toothed or entire ...............   29. Rhamnaceae
          Fruit a nut, capsule, samara
          or achene, not fleshy:
              Fruit papery, conspicuous-
              ly winged:
                  Leaves entire, glutinous
                  when young; fruit often
tinged pink-purple   .................. 30a. Sapindaceae
                  Leaves toothed; fruit
                  pale green .............................   85. Ulmaceae
              Fruit not papery or
              winged:
                  Flowers unisexual, the
                  males forming deciduous
                  catkins:
                      Plants dioecious;
                      seeds enveloped in
                      a silky tuft of hairs...............   92. Salicaceae
                      Plants monoecious;
                      seeds without a silky
                      tuft of hairs:
                          Fruit enveloped in
                          a spiny husk or seat-
                          ed in a scaly
                          cupule............................   91. Fagaceae
                          Fruit without a spiny
                          husk or scaly
                          cupule:
```

Fruit an ovoid nut,
enveloped by a
foliaceous invo-
lucre .... 90. Corylaceae
Fruit without a fo-
liaceous involucre 89. Betulaceae
Flowers hermaphrodite
or, if unisexual, males
not forming catkins:
Flowers greenish, in-
conspicuous 74.Chenopodiaceae
Flowers coloured,
conspicuous:
Fruit woody, persis-
tent, conspicuous .... 79a. Proteaceae
Fruit not woody,
inconspicuous,
often hidden in the
persistent perianth........... 80. Thymelaeaceae

GROUP G
HERBS WITH ALTERNATE OR BASAL, COMPOUND OR DEEPLY DIVIDED
LEAVES
Leaves all basal:
Flowers crowded into a dense spike .... 72. Plantaginaceae
Flowers not in a spike:
Leaves 3-foliolate; leaflets obcordate .... 27. Oxalidaceae
Leaves not 3-foliolate; leaflets not obcor-
date:
Ovary inferior; flowers in umbels .... 45. Umbelliferae
Ovary superior; flowers not in umbels:
Carpels united until ripe, with a central
beak... 26. Ceraniaceae
Carpels free, sometimes individually
beaked but without a central beak......................... 4. Ranunculaceae
Leaves not all basal:
Flowers with a distinct calyx and corolla:
Petals free:
Petals 4 or fewer:
Stamens numerous:
Flowers actinomorphic; stems exu-
ding latex when broken .... 7. Papaveraceae
Flowers zygomorphic; stem not
exuding latex when broken .... 4. Ranunculaceae
Stamens 6 or fewer:
Petals all similar, equal or subequal:
Leaves palmately compound........................ 10. Capparaceae

Leaves pinnately or irregularly dis-
sected or lobed .... 9. Cruciferae
Petals in dissimilar, unequal pairs:
Flowers spurred or saccate, in
racemes or spikes .... 8. Fumariaceae
Flowers not spurred, solitary or
in cymes .... 7. Papaveraceae
Petals 5 or more:
Flowers zygomorphic:
Ovary superior:
Sepals united into a basal tube;
fruit a pod.. 33. Leguminosae
Sepals free or almost free; fruit
a capsule .... 11. Resedaceae
Ovary inferior ....45. Umbelliferae
Flowers actinomorphic:
Leaves and stems stellate-pilose..................... 23. Malvaceae
Leaves and stems not stellate-pi-
lose:
Leaves dotted over with translu-
cent glands .... 28. Rutaceae
Leaves not gland-dotted:
Leaves trifoliolate with obcor-
date leaflets... 27. Oxalidaceae
Leaves not trifoliolate:
Leaves paripinnate............................. 25. Zygophyllaceae
Leaves not paripinnate:
Fruit of 2 or more free
achenes or follicles:
Land plants:
Cauline leaves stipulate   34. Rosaceae
Cauline leaves exstipu-
late:
Sepals unequal, grading
into petals; fruit consi-
sting of 2 or more lea-
thery or fleshy follicles .... 5. Paeoniaceae
Sepals equal or sube-
qual, not grading into
petals; fruit not leathe-
ery or fleshy .... 4. Ranunculaceae
Water plants; leaves with
capillary divisions .... 4. Ranunculaceae
Fruit not apocarpous; car-
pels fused at least until maturity:
Fruit with a central beak............. 26. Geraniaceae

Fruit without a central
beak .... 35. Saxifragaceae
Petals united into a tube:
  Plants with tendrils; fruit large, fleshy,
  indehiscent .... 43. Cucurbitaceae
  Plants without tendrils; fruit not as
  above:
    Flowers zygomorphic... 67.Scrophulariaceae
    Flowers actinomorphic:
      Flowers in scorpioid cymes .... 6a. Hydrophyllaceae
      Flowers solitary or paired, axillary..................... 65. Convolvulaceae
Flowers without a distinct calyx and corolla:
  Leaves palmate; shoots and young leaves
  resinous, aromatic... 85a. Cannabaceae
  Leaves pinnate, pinnatisect or irregularly
  laciniate:
    Leaves imparipinnate; fruit a pendulous
    capsule... 42. Datiscaceae
    Leaves not imparipinnate; fruit a small
    nut or achene:
      Perianth-segments 5; plants erect,
      glandular-aromatic.. 74.Chenopodiaceae
      Perianth-segments 4; plants prostrate,
      not aromatic.. 34. Rosaceae

GROUP H
HERBS WITH SIMPLE, ALTERNATE LEAVES, OR LEAVES ALL BASAL
Flowers with a distinct calyx and corolla:
  Petals free:
  Indumentum of stellate hairs:
    Petals 4 .... 9. Cruciferae
    Petals 5 or more:
      Flowers conspicuous; fruit a schizocarp
      or 5-locular capsule .... 22. Malvaceae
      Flowers inconspicuous; fruit 3-locular................... 83. Euphorbiaceae
  Indumentum of simple hairs or plants
  glabrous:
    Flowers actinomorphic:
      Petals 3; sepals 3 .... 102. Alismataceae
      Petals and sepals 4 or more:
        Ovary inferior or semi-inferior:
          Flowers in simple or compound
          umbels.. 45. Umbelliferae
          Flowers not in umbels:
            Seeds with a coma of silky hairs   41. Onagraceae
            Seeds without a coma of silky
            hairs:

Style 1, bifid... 53. Compositae
Styles 2 or more:
  Styles 2, divergent, like
    minute horns.................................. 39. Saxifragaceae
  Styles 3 or more .... 44. Aizoaceae
Ovary superior:
  Fruit apocarpous, comprising a
  group of achenes or follicles:
    Leaves fleshy.......................... 36. Crassulaceae
    Leaves not fleshy.................... 4. Ranunculaceae
  Fruit not apocarpous; carpels uni-
  ted at least until maturity:
    Petals and sepals 4................ 9. Cruciferae
    Petals and sepals usually 5 or
    more:
      Fruits with a central beak .... 26. Geraniaceae
      Fruits without a central beak:
        Leaves glandular-punctate,
        strong-smelling when
        crushed... 28. Rutaceae
        Leaves not glandular-pun-
        ctate or strong-smelling:
          Fruit woody, spinose .... 34. Rosaceae
          Fruit not woody or spinose:
            Fruit a circumscissile
            capsule .... 18. Portulacaceae
            Fruit not circumscissile:
              Fruit dehiscing into 10,
              1-seeded valves............... 24. Linaceae
              Fruit a 1-6-locular
              capsule:
                Style simple, filiform:
                  Sepals free or
                  almost free;
                  stamens nume-
                  rous .... 23. Tiliaceae
                  Sepals united into
                  a tube; stamens 12
                  or fewer .... 40. Lythraceae
                Styles 3-5, free or
                partly connate............ 44. Aizoaceae
Flowers zygomorphic:
  Lowermost petal spurred or saccate
  at base; flowers solitary .... 13. Violaceae
  Lowermost petal not spurred or sac-
  cate at base; flowers in spikes or
  racemes:

Lowermost petal with a conspicuous
fimbriate apex... 14. Polygalaceae
Lowermost petal without a fimbriate
apex:
    Fruit a pod .... 33. Leguminosae
    Fruit a capsule, open and gaping
    at apex.. 11. Resedaceae
Petals united:
  Flowers distinctly zygomorphic:
    Leaves all basal; flowers solitary:
      Leaves densely viscid-glandular
      above.. 69. Lentibulariaceae
      Leaves not viscid-glandular 67.Scrophulariaceae
    Leaves not all basal:
      Flowers solitary.................................... 54. Campanulaceae
      Flowers in inflorescences:
        Fruit a nutlet; leaves strigose or
        bristly.. 64. Boraginaceae
        Fruit a capsule; leaves not strigose
        or bristly:
          Leaves clammy-glandular............ 66. Solanaceae
          Leaves not clammy-glandular:
            Capsule oblong-quadrangular.................. 69b. Pedaliaceae
            Capsule not oblong-quadran-
            gular.. 67.Scrophulariaceae
  Flowers actinomorphic or almost so:
    Ovary inferior:
      Flowers unisexual; fruit fleshy............................... 43. Cucurbitaceae
      Flowers hermaphrodite; fruit a capsule 54. Campanulaceae
    Ovary superior:
      Styles 5, free or partly connate .... 57. Plumbaginaceae
      Style 1, simple or shortly bifid at apex:
        Corolla scarious, brownish or
        greenish; capsule circumscissile...................... 72. Plantaginaceae
        Corolla not scarious, not brownish
        or greenish:
          Corolla funnel-shaped:
            Fruit woody, usually spinose .... 66. Solanaceae
            Fruit not woody or spinose...................... 65. Convolvulaceae
          Corolla not funnel-shaped:
            Corolla narrowly tubular .... 66. Solanaceae
           Corolla not narrowly tubular:
              Fruit a berry.. 66. Solanaceae
             Fruit a capsule:
                Capsule circumscissile .... 66. Solanaceae
                Capsule not
                circumscissile:

Leaves hairy:
    Flowers in spikes or
    racemes.................................. 67.Scrophulariaceae
    Flowers not in spikes or
    racemes.............................. 65. Convolvulaceae
Leaves glabrous or very
sparsely pubescent................... 58. Primulaceae
Flowers without a distinct calyx and corolla:
  Submerged or floating aquatics:
    Plants growing in the sea:
      Rhizomes covered with dense fibres
      from persistent, decayed leaf-sheaths .... 106. Posidoniaceae
      Rhizomes not densely fibrous:
        Leaves in congested, terminal tufts;
        apex sharply serrulate; basal sheaths
        conspicuous..108.Cymodoceaceae
        Leaves not in terminal tufts, apex not
        serrulate.. 107a. Zosteraceae
    Plants growing in fresh water:
      Perianth well developed, of 4 segments;
      flowers often numerous in pedunculate
      spikes

      .... 104.Potamogetonaceae
      Perianth absent or much reduced:
        Fruits borne at the apex of a long,
        slender (often spirally twisted)
        peduncle .... 105. Rubiaceae
        Fruits sessile or shortly stipitate:
          Leaves entire or subentire; fruits
          keeled, usually crenate or dentate
          dorsally.. 107.Zannichelliaceae
          Leaves serrulate; fruits not keeled,
          not crenate or dentate dorsally......................... 105a. Najadaceae
Terrestrial plants, or, if aquatic, not floating
or submerged:
  Inflorescence consisting of a fleshy cylindrical spadix, surrounded by a spathe;
  leaves usually all basal, sagittate.................................... 101. Araceae
  Inflorescence not consisting of a spadix
  and spathe:
    Flowers without any obvious perianth:
      Flowers unisexual forming readily
      distinguishable inflorescences on the
      same plant (monoecious):
        Inflorescences dense, cylindrical,
        terminal on stout erect, unbranched
        stems; female inflorescences velu-

tinous, dark brown.. 99. Typhaceae
Inflorescences not as above:
   Inflorescences globose; stems
     terete .... 100. Sparganiaceae
   Inflorescences not globose:
     Stems terete; female flowers
     enveloped by papery, spatha-
     ceous sheaths... 110. Gramineae
     Stems trigonous; female flowers
     not enveloped by spathaceous
     sheaths .... 109. Cyperaceae
Flowers hermaphrodite, or, if unisexual
not forming distinct inflorescences:
   Stems mostly hollow except at the
   well-marked nodes; leaf-sheaths open,
   separated from blade by a distinct
   articulation; styles 2, distinct .... 110. Gramineae
   Stems pith-filled, without obvious nodes,
   often trigonous or triquestrous; leaf-
   sheath usually tubular, closed, not
   clearly separated from blade; style
   1, often divided into branches
   above .... 109. Cyperaceae
Flowers with a well-developed
perianth:
   Ovary inferior:
     Plant tree-like in habit with very large
     oblong leaves... 93a. Musaceae
     Plant not tree-like in habit:
       Leaves thick, fleshy, with spinose
       margins.. 95a. Agavaceae
       Leaves not spinose-margined:
         Leaves cordate, reniform or
         lobed:
           Perianth tubular, zygomor-
           phic... 78. Aristolochiaceae
           Perianth not tubular, actino-
           morphic.. 96. Dioscoreaceae
         Leaves not cordate, reniform
         or lobed:
           Flowers zygomorphic:
             Stamens 3 with filaments
             and anthers.................................... 94. Iridaceae
             Stamens 1-2, sessile, pollen
             generally agglutinated into
             masses (pollinia)........................... 93. Orchidaceae
           Flowers actinomorphic or

almost actinomorphic:
    Perianth small, inconspi-
    cuous, greenish; fruit inde-
    hiscent .... 82. Santalaceae
    Perianth conspicuous, white
    or coloured:
        Stamens 3 .... 94. Iridaceae
        Stamens 6 .... 95. Amaryllidaceae
Ovary superior:
    Leaves lanceolate, linear or subulate
    with parallel nerves (monocotyledons):
        Perianth conspicuous, white or
        brightly coloured .... 97. Liliaceae
        Perianth inconspicuous, membranous
        or glumaceous:
            Inflorescence spicate; carpels 3,
            free; styles wanting .... 103. Juncaginaceae
            Inflorescence not spicate; carpels
            united; styles present .... 98. Juncaceae
    Leaves not lanceolate, linear or subu-
    late; nervation not parallel (dicotyledons):
        Stems climbing; flowers in tail-like
        spikes .... 74a. Basellaceae
        Stems not climbing:
            Fruit a black juicy berry .... 75. Phytolaccaceae
            Fruit not a juicy berry:
                Stipules united into a membra-
                nous, tubular sheath (ochrea)
                around the stem .... 76. Polygonaceae
                Stipules not united into a mem-
                branous, tubular sheath, or
                plants exstipulate:
                    Fruit 2-3 locular .... 83. Euphorbiaceae
                    Fruit 1-locular, circumscissile
                    or indehiscent:
                        Perianth membranous .... 73. Amaranthaceae
                        Perianth herbaceous or
                        fleshy:
                            Stigma penicillate .... 84. Urticaceae
                            Stigma not penicillate .... 74. Chenopodiaceae

1. Pinaceae Family

Pinus nigra ssp. pallasiana (Black pine or Mandópefkos)

A tree with a columnar trunk on which the branches are set more or less in whorls. Needles rigid 6-10 cm. long, in pairs on a common short-shoot. Cones 6-8 cm. long. Pinus nigra forms forests on the upper slopes of the Troodos Range, particularly on Hionistra Peak up to altitudes of about 1.900 m.

Pinus brutia (Calabrian pine or Péfkos)

A tree with a somewhat columnar trunk. The crown of young trees is pyramidal but later becomes irregular in shape. Needles in pairs 11-16 cm long. Cones 5-11 cm. long, subsessile, growing at right angles to branches. The most common forest tree of Cyprus, Pinus brutia forms large forests from sea level to the montane zone, in the regions of the Troodos Range, Karpassia, Akamas and the Pendadahtilos Range.

Other species of the Pinaceae Family introduced to Cyprus and cultivated or used in reforestations are: **Pinus pinea, Pinus halepensis, Pinus radiata, Pinus canariensis, Abies cephalonica, Abies alba, Abies cilicica.**

Top: branch with leaves (needles) and cone of Pinus nigra ssp. pallasiana. Bottom: branch with cones and needles of the Calabrian pine (Pinus brutia)

Cedrus libanii ssp. brevifolia (Cyprus cedar or Kédros tis Kíprou)

A tree with a columnar trunk and spreading branches. Needles narrow, rigid, seldom more than 15 mm. long. Cones erect, barrel-shaped, up to 8 cm. long. This tree is endemic to Cyprus; it forms forests on the western summits of the Troodos Range, but has been planted successfully in other places. Many Cyprus cedars have also been planted in Greece, several in the Mt. Parnitha National Park, and a few in the Kesarianí Aesthetic Forest.

2. Cupressaceae Family

Cupressus sempervirens var. horizontalis (Italian cypress or Kiparíssi thilikó)

A large tree with dull green leaves and spreading branches. Cones 2-3 cm. long, almost spherical, with few scales. A long-lived tree, often reaching an age of over a thousand years, well-known for its rot-resistant, valuable wood. In Cyprus it grows in the Pendadahtilos Range, in Karpassia, the western part of the Troodos Range and in the region of Akamas.

Species introduced into Cyprus for cultivation or reforestation are the following: **Cupressus sempervirens var. sempervirens, Cupressus arizonica, Cupressus macrocarpa,** and **Cupressus guadalupensis.**

Top: branches and needles of the Cyprus cedar (Cedrus libanii ssp. brevifolia). Bottom: branches of Cupressus sempervirens var. horizontalis with scale-like leaves and male flowers.

Juniperus foetidissima (Stinking juniper or Aóratos)

A long-lived tree of medium height with a pyramidal crown. Similar to the cypress but more densely branched. Leaves small overlapping scales. Cones very small (8-10 mm.), indehiscent, globose, dark purple when mature. This species forms a small forest on Hionistra Peak in the Troodos Range.

Other species of Juniper growing in Cyprus are **Juniperus excelsa, Juniperus oxycedrus ssp. oxycedrus, Juniperus oxycedrus ssp. macrocarpa** and **Juniperus phoenicea.**

Two species of the Taxodiaceae Family have been introduced into the Troodos range sporadically. These are **Sequoia sempervirens** and **Sequoiadendron giganteum.**

3. Ephedraceae Family

Ephedra fragilis ssp. campylopoda (Polikómbi)

A dioecious perennial plant with long slender greenish stems. Leaves tiny, scale-like. Female plants produce red fleshy fruits 5-7 mm. long. This species grows throughout Cyprus in rocky places in the lowlands and sub-montane zone.

The rare species **Ephedra major** also grows in Cyprus, in the Troodos Range.

Top: branches, leaves and male flowers of the Stinking juniper (Juniperus foeti dissima). Bottom: Ephedra fragilis ssp. campylopoda. Branches and fruits of a female plant.

4. Ranunculaceae Family

Anemone coronaria (Anemóna or Mavromata)

A plant with large flowers (3-8 cm.), leaves all basal, divided into many narrow lobes. Below the flowers, which have 5-7 coloured sepals and no petals, is an involucre of 3 whorled bracts, also narrowly lobed. There are many varieties, with rose-pink, scarlet, blue or whitish flowers. Anthers purplish or black. Common in lowlands. Flowers December-April.

Anemone blanda (Anemóna tou vounoú)

A plant similar to Anemone coronaria but sepals more numerous (9-15), lanceolate, blue, mauve, pink or white. Basal leaves reddish below, deeply cut into narrow lobes. Involucral bracts similar to basal leaves. This species grows in the forests and fields of the Troodos and Pendadahtilos Ranges. Flowers February-April.

Ranunculus asiaticus (Nerangoúla agria)

A plant with perennial roots. Stem 5-30 cm. high, pubescent-villose, sparsely branched. Leaves usually 3-lobed, pubescent-villose. Flowers 2.5-7 cm. diam., sepals villose, petals large, white, red, pinkish or yellow. Common in Cyprus outside of the Troodos Range. Flowers March-May. See following pages.

Top: one of the many varieties of Anemone coronaria. Bottom: flowers and leaves of Anemone blanda.

Ranunculus ficaria ssp. ficariiformis

Tubers perennial. Stems and leaves appear in winter. Leaves reniform or broadly ovate. Basal leaves 4-6 cm. long. Stems are short and flowers large, 3,5-6 cm. diam. Petals 9-12, yellow. Sepals 3. This species grows in damp pastures throughout Cyprus. More common in the mountains. Flowers March-May.

The following species of genus Ranunculus may also be found in Cyprus: **Ranunculus peltatus ssp. peltatus, Ranunculus peltatus ssp. sphaerospermus, Ranunculus bullatus ssp. cytheraeus, Ranunculus rumelicus, Ranunculus cadmicus var. cyprius, Ranunculus kykkoensis, Ranunculus neapolitanus var. adpresse-pilosus, Ranunculus chius, Ranunculus millefolius, Ranunculus millefoliatus ssp. leptaleus.**

The genus Adonis is represented in Cyprus by the species: **Adonis annua, Adonis aestivalis, Adonis microcarpa** and **Adonis dentata.** Members of the Clematis genus found in Cyprus are **Clematis cirrhosa, Clematis viticella** and **Clematis vitalba.**

Top: Ranunculus asiaticus. The white-flowered variety is the most common in Cyprus. Bottom: flowers and leaves of Ranunculus ficaria ssp. ficariiformis.

Consolida ambigua (Gatoúles)

Erect annual up to 60 cm. or more in height. Stems simple or branched, pubescent-villose. Leaves dissected into numerous linear or filiform lobes. Inflorescence a raceme. Flowers have 5 sepals and 4 petals, all coloured, usually violet, or more rarely pink, with an adaxial spur. Rare in cultivated fields around Limassol. Flowers May-June.

Other species belonging to the Ranunculaceae Family which grow in Cyprus are: **Consolida phrygia, Delphinium peregrinum var. eriocarpum, Delphinium caseyi, Delphinium staphisagria, Garidella nigellastrum, Garidella unguicularis, Nigella damascena, Nigella arvensis, Nigella sativa, Nigella ciliaris and Nigella fumariifolia.**

Opposite page: Consolida ambigua, also known as Delphinium ajacis, is one of the loveliest spring flowers. It is often planted in gardens in Cyprus and Greece as an ornamental plant known as "Gatoúles" (Little cats).

5. Paeoniaceae Family

Paeonia mascula ssp. mascula (Pigounia or Triandafilon tou Livadioú)

A plant with a perennial rhizome. Stem erect, 30-60 cm. high. Leaves 4-7, large, divided into three leaflets, each of which is in turn composed of broad, obovate or elliptical leaflets or lobes. Petioles 5-12 cm. long. Flowers 6,5-10 cm. diam., rosy-purple. Petals 5-6, obovate or orbicular. Stamens numerous, yellow. Sepals 3-5. A rare species growing in the Troodos Range. Flowers April-May.

6. Berberidaceae Family

Leontice leontopetalum (Foúska or Voidokratis)

Erect plant, glabrous, with a perennial globose rhizome. Stem 15-60 cm. high. Leaves large, glaucous, the long-stalked divisions larger, divided into leaflets broadly ovate, orbicular or trilobate. Inflorescence large, pyramidal. Flowers yellow with petals and sepals together 6-8. Fruit large, papery, bladder-like, 3-4 cm. long. Grows in lowlands and sub-montane zone. Flowers February-April.

Other members of the same family which grow in Cyprus are **Berberis cretica** and **Bongardia chrysogonum.**

Top: The Peony (Paeonia mascula ssp. mascula) is one of the most impressive wild flowers of Cyprus. Bottom: Leontice leontopetalum, a fairly common plant in fields.

7. Papaveraceae Family

Papaver rhoeas var. oblongatum (Paparoúna)

An annual herb with stems 10-30 cm. high, hispid, with patent or rarely adpressed hairs. Basal leaves narrowly obovate or oblanceolate, pinnatisect or pinnatipartite, hispid, petiolate, 7-20 cm. long; petiole 3-10 cm. long, narrowly winged. Stem leaves similar but smaller, petiolate or sessile. Flowers large, red. Petals with or without a black blotch at the base. Capsule obovate, gradually narrowing toward the base. Anthers black. Scattered throughout the island from sea level to about 1.200 m. alt., in fallow and cultivated fields. Flowers March-June. A variety with 6 petals and capsules broader, subglobose, grows on the summit "Throní tis Panagías", where Archbishop Makarios is buried, above the Kiko Monastery.

Papaver postii

A small plant with one or more slender stems up to 20 cm. high. Leaves small, strigose, forming a rosette at the base, pinnatifid or lyrate, lobes acute or subacute. Flowers 2-4 cm. diam. Petals light scarlet or light orange. Capsule glabrous, oblong, subclavate. Troodos Range. Locally present between 500 and 1.200 m. alt. Flowers April - May. See following pages.

Top: Papaver rhoeas var. oblongatum. Bottom: the 6-petalled variety which grows on Archbishop Makarios' grave.

Papaver hybridum (Anginaróhorto)

A tall plant, with rather slender stems and sparse branches. Can be distinguished from the other species of Papaver by its ellipsoid capsules covered with dense, rigid bristles. Leaves pinnatisect with dentate or pinnately-lobed divisions. Flowers small, 2-5 cm. diam., purplish-red. Petals blotched black at the base. Grows in fields throughout almost the entire island. Flowers March-May.

Other species of the genus Papaver which grow in Cyprus are **Papaver dubium, Papaver argemone ssp. meiklii, Papaver somniferum ssp. setigerum, Papaver guerlekense, Papaver minus, Papaver gracile.**

Other members of the Papaveraceae family found in Cyprus are **Roemeria hybrida, Hypecoum procumbens, Hypecoum imberbe and Hypecoum pendulum.**

Top: Papaver postii, an Asiatic species of poppy which grows in the mountains of Cyprus. Bottom: Papaver hybridum, known by its common name Anginaróhorto.

Glaucium flavum var. leiocarpum (Gialópikro or Gialópetro)

A tall plant, up to 80 cm. high. Basal leaves pinnatisect, 10-20 cm. long, stem leaves smaller. Flowers axillary and terminal. Buds 1.5-2.5 cm. long, acuminate. Sepals glabrous. Petals tawny-yellow or rarely reddish, 2-3 cm. long. Anthers yellow. Capsule a narrow siliqua, usually not longer than 20 cm. Grows on sandy ground near the sea, in the region of Larnaca. Flowers May-August.

Aside from the above species, **Glaucium corniculatum** is also found in Cyprus, together with its three varieties: **var. flaviflorum, var. tricolor** and **var. corniculatum.**

8. Fumariaceae Family

Corydalis rutifolia (Hionístra)

A plant with stems 6-20 cm. high. Flowers pink. Leaves 2-3, opposite or whorled, pinnately or bipinnately lobed, glabrous and rather glaucous. This western Asian species grows only on Tripilos and Hionistra Peaks in the Troodos Range. Flowers April-May.

Other species of the Fumariaceae Family which grow in Cyprus are the following: **Ceratocapnos palaestinus, Fumaria gaillardotii, Fumaria judaica, Fumaria macrocarpa, Fumaria capreolata, Fumaria petteri ssp. thuretti, Fumaria officinales, Fumaria densiflora, Fumaria bracteosa, Fumaria parviflora.**

Top: Glaucium flavum var. leiocarpum, known as Gialópikro or Gialópetro. Bottom: Corydalis rutifolia, which grows on the summits of the Troodos Range.

9. Cruciferae Family

Alyssum troodi

A small, perennial subshrub, 10-25 cm. high. Leaves 5-10 mm. long, ob-ovate-spatulate, covered with a silvery indumentum. Flowering and sterile shoots co-exist on the same plant. On the sterile shoots the leaves form terminal clusters. Flowers have golden-yellow petals, 3 mm. long. Siliques elliptic, glabrous, 7-8 mm. long. Endemic to the Troodos Range, from 1.300 m. alt. to the highest summit of Hionistra. Flowers May-July.

Alyssum cypricum

Similar to Alyssum troodi, but siliques ovate or obovate-elliptic, up to 4 mm. long, covered with an indumentum of silvery stellate hairs and obtuse at both ends. Grows in the Troodos Range between 1.100 and 1.890 m. alt. Flowers April-June. This species is also found in Turkey.

Other species of the Alyssum genus which grow in Cyprus are the following: **Alyssum akamasicum, Alyssum chondrogynum, Alyssum minus, Alyssum strigosum, Alyssum umbellatum, Alyssum minutum, Alyssum foliosum.**

Top: Alyssum troodi, an endemic common in the higher reaches of the Troodos Range. Bottom: Alyssum cypricum, which also grows in the mountains of SW Turkey.

Arabis purpurea

A perennial herb with copious stems. Basal leaves form rosettes. Leaves densely tomentose, obovate-spatulate, small. Flowers pink or purplish, rarely white. Siliques linear. This plant is a local endemic of the Troodos Range, from 600 to 1.450 m. alt. Grows in clefts in rocks. Flowers March-May.

Arabis verna

An erect annual, 10-15 (-30) cm. high. Stems and leaves stellate-pilose. Basal leaves obovate-oblong, apex obtuse, margins slightly serrate forming a compact rosette. Stem leaves much smaller, ovate, acute, sessile or amplexicaul. Flowers purple or violet, petals 7-9 mm. long, glabrous **(var. verna)** or pubescent **(var. dasycarpa).** Grows in regions of the Troodos Range, Paphos, Limassol and Kyrenia, up to 1.300 m. alt. Flowers February-May.

The species **Arabis kennedyae** and **Arabis cypria** also grow in Cyprus.

Top: Arabis purpurea, one of the most beautiful endemic plants of the Troodos Range. Bottom: Arabis verna.

Sinapis arvensis (Lapsana)

A simple or branched annual up to 80 cm. high. Leaves subglabrous or hispid, obovate or lyrate-pinnatifid. Inflorescence racemose with yellow flowers. Petals 8-12 mm. long. There are three varieties: a) typical (**arvensis**) with siliques somewhat erect, glabrous, 2,5-4 cm. long, b) var. **orientalis,** covered with white bristles and c) var. **schkuhriana** with siliques 4-5,5 cm. long, slender, often bent or twisted. This plant is widely distributed throughout Cyprus on cultivated and waste ground, up to 1.500 m. alt. Flowers March-September.

Other species of the Sinapis genus which grow in Cyprus are **Sinapis alba ssp. alba** and **Sinapis alba ssp. mairei.**

Raphanus raphanistrum (Agriorapanída)

Annual or biennial herb, hispid, erect. Stems much branched, up to 60 cm. high. Lower leaves large, lyrate; upper leaves smaller, simple. Sepals 8-10 mm. long and petals 12-20 mm. long, white or sometimes pink with dark veins. Siliques 30-90 mm. long, constricted between seeds, with a slender terminal beak. Grows in regions of the Troodos Range, Larnaca, Famagusta, Nicosia, Morphou and Kyrenia, up to 250 m. alt. Flowers February-April.

Raphanus sativus, cultivated for its edible root, often escapes from cultivation and grows wild in Cyprus.

Top: Sinapis arvensis, also known by its common name Lapsana. Bottom: Raphanus raphanistrum, known as Agriorapanída.

Matthiola incana (Violéta)

Perennial 25-50 cm. high, greyish green, clothed in a stellate indumentum. Stem woody near the base. Leaves simple, oblanceolate, rarely pinnatifid or pinnatipartite. Flowers large. Sepals 9-13 mm. long, petals 20-30 mm. long, purple, pink or mauve, rarely white. Siliques linear, 45-160 mm. long. Grows on rocks in the littoral and lowlands, in the Larnaca-Famagusta region. Rare. This species is often cultivated in gardens. Different varieties include those with white, purple, mauve or pink flowers, double or single. Flowers February-May.

Matthiola sinuata (Agriovioléta)

Similar to **Matthiola incana** but leaves lobed-sinuate and petals smaller (16-20 mm. long), light mauve. A plant common in the Mediterranean area but rare in Cyprus, where it has been collected only twice near the seashore. Flowers February-April.

Other species of the Matthiola genus which grow in Cyprus are **Matthiola tricuspidata, Matthiola fruticulosa** and **Matthiola longipetala.**

Top: Matthiola incana, known by its common name of Violéta. Bottom: Matthiola sinuata or Agriovioléta, common in other Mediterranean countries but very rare in Cyprus.

Malcolmia flexuosa (Agriovioléta)

A much-branched plant, 4-15 cm. high. Leaves slightly fleshy, obovate or spatulate, 20-50 mm. long. Inflorescence a rather short raceme, with pink, mauve or white flowers. Petals 12-17 mm. long. Siliques spreading, 35-50 mm. long and 12-17 mm. wide. Grows on rocks near the seashore, in the regions of Morphou and Kyrenia. Flowers February-May.

Other species of the genus Malcolmia growing in Cyprus are **Malcolmia chia var. chia, Malcolmia chia var. lyrata, Malcolmia nana var. nana, Malcolmia nana var. glabra.**

Other members of the Cruciferae Family which grow in Cyprus: **Nasturtium officinale, Turritis laxa, Erysimum repandum, Alliaria petiolata, Sisymbrium irio, Sisymbrium orientale, Sisymbrium officinale, Sisymbrium polyceratium, Torularia torulosa, Arabidopsis thaliana, Camelina rumelica, Carrichtera annua, Enarthrocarpus arcuatus, Enarthrocarpus lyratus, Calepina irregularis, Crambe hispanica, Rapistrum rugosum, Didesmus aegyptius, Erucaria hispanica, Cakile maritima, Conringia orientalis, Brassica hilarionis, Brassica tournefortii, Brassica nigra, Erophila verna, Erophila minima, Cardamine graeca, Cardamine hirsuta, Lobularia maritima, Lobularia libyca, Clypeola jonthlaspi, Lepidium spinosum, Lepidium sativum, Lepidium perfoliatum, Lepidium latifolium, Teesdalia coronopifolia, Cardaria drapa, Iberis odorata, Biscutella didyma, Thlaspi cyprium, Thlaspi perfoliatum, Capsella bursa-pastoris, Hymenolobus procumbens, Ochtodium aegyptiacum, Neslia apiculata, Fibigia eriocarpa, Eruca vesicaria, Hirschfeldia incana, Diplotaxis viminea.**

Opposite page: Malcolmia flexuosa, also known by its common name of Agriovioléta, a species common in Mediterranean countries, where it always grows near the seashore.

10. Capparaceae Family

Capparis spinosa (Kapari or Kaparka)

Plant with a perennial root. Stems long, spreading, spinose, appearing in spring and summer. Leaves ovate-orbicular, slightly fleshy, 1,5-5 cm. long. Flowers large (4-6 cm. diam.), white or tinged pink, with 4 petals and numerous long stamens. Grows on rocky land in the lowland, submontane and littoral zones. Flowers May-August.

Other members of the Capparaceae Family growing in Cyprus are **Cleome ornithopodioides** and **Cleome iberica.**

Opposite page: Capparis spinosa, with its impressive flowers which bloom during the driest season of the year, is really a marvel of nature. Its buds, tender stems and fruit are pickled in salt, vinegar and olive oil to make a very tasty appetiser.

11. Resedaceae Family

Reseda lutea (Resenda or Óhra)

An annual or perennial with erect stems, 20-60 cm. high. Leaves impari-pinnatisect, with 1-4 lobes on each side. Flowers small, yellowish, form-ing racemes. Petals 6, fringed on adaxial margin. Sepals 6. Grows in hills at low and intermediate altitudes throughout the island. Flowers February-September.

Other species of the Reseda genus growing in Cyprus: **Reseda alba, Reseda luteola, Reseda orientalis, Reseda odorata.**

12. Cistaceae Family

Cistus creticus (Ladania or Kounouklia or Leoudia)

A small aromatic shrub, up to 1 m. high. Leaves ovate, obovate or ellip-tic, hoary-glandular, 15-25 mm. long. Flowers pink-purplish, 4-6 cm diam. Stamens yellow. Common on hills and slopes at low and intermedi-ate altitudes. From the aromatic leaves of this plant, "labdanum", an aro-matic, medicinal resin, was extracted in former times. Flowers March-June.

Top: Reseda lutea, whose common name is Óhra (ochre), because it was once used to dye fabrics yellow. Bottom: Cistus creticus or Ladania or Leoudia, a shrub fairly common in the lowlands and sub-montane zone.

Cistus salviifolius

Similar to Cistus creticus but flowers white, slightly smaller (3-5 cm diam.) and leaves less hairy and greener. Grows in garigue and forest at low and intermediate altitudes throughout the island, including the montane zone of Troodos. Flowers February-May.

The species **Cistus monspeliensis, Cistus parviflorus** and **Cistus ladanifer** are also found in Cyprus.

Helianthemum syriacum

A perennial sub-shrub, leaves opposite, 1-3,5 cm. long, lanceolate or ovate. Flowers yellow, 15-20 mm. diam., in compound corymbose inflorescences. This species grows in the regions of Akamas, Troodos, Dekelia, Kyrenia, Rizokarpasso, etc. Flowers April-June.

Other species of the genus Helianthemum growing in Cyprus are **Helianthemum chamaecistus, Helianthemum obtusifolium, Helianthemum stipulatum, Helianthemum salicifolium, Helianthemum ledifolium, Helianthemum aegyptiacum.**

Top: White-flowered Cistus salviifolius is more common in Cyprus than Cistus creticus. Bottom: Helianthemum syriacum.

Fumana thymifolia

A sub-shrub with slender, woody stems and alternate leaves, ovate or lanceolate, 10-12 mm. long. Flowers yellow, 15-20 mm. diam., solitary. This species grows in garigue and maquis at low altitudes. Flowers March-June.

The species **Fumana arabica** also grows in Cyprus.

Violaceae Family

Viola rauliniana

A dwarf species. Leaves very small, ovate, subentire or slightly dentate. Stipules smaller than the leaves, entire. Flowers yellowish-white, with a yellow blotch at the base of the lowermost petal; about 1 cm. diam. This plant grows on the summits of the Troodos Range, as well as in the mountains of Crete. Flowers April-June.

Viola sieheana

Perennial with stems 15-30 cm. high. Leaves cordate, petiolate, 1,5-5 cm. long. Flowers 2 cm. diam.; petals bluish-violet, spur white. Stipules lanceolate, subentire. Fairly common in forests of the Troodos Range. Flowers March-May. See following pages.

Top: Fumana thymifolia, a delightful small shrub with yellow flowers which grow in hills and garigue. Bottom: Viola rauliniana, a dwarf species that grows on the summits of the Troodos Range.

Other members of the Viola genus which grow in Cyprus are **Viola kitai-beliama, Viola odorata** and **Viola alba.**

14. Polygalaceae Family

Only two members of this family grow in Cyprus, **Polygala monspeliaca** and **Polygala venulosa.**

15. Frankeniaceae Family

Two insignificant species belonging to this family grow in Cyprus, **Frankenia pulverulenta** and **Frankenia hirsuta.**

16. Caryophyllaceae Family

Arenaria rhodia ssp. cypria

An annual with ovate-orbicular, opposite leaves. Petals white, entire, 4-6 mm. long. Endemic to Cyprus: regions of Akamas and Troodos. Flowers March-May.

Other species of the Arenaria genus found in Cyprus are **Arenaria pamphylica ssp. kyrenica, Arenaria leptoclados** and **Arenaria saponarioides.**

Top: Viola sieheana, which grows in the forests of the Troodos Range. Bottom: Arenaria rhodia ssp. cypria, a plant endemic to Cyprus.

Silene laevigata

A dwarf plant, glabrous, glaucous, with small, pink flowers. Petals bifid, 9-10 mm. long. An endemic of the Troodos Range. Flowers March-May.

Silene colorata

A pubescent annual, 10-50 cm. high. Leaves spatulate, ovate or linear. Petals large, pink or purple, bifid. A common plant in fields and waste land at low altitudes outside the Troodos Range. Flowers February-May.

Other members of the Silene genus growing in Cyprus are **Silene fruticosa, Silene gigantea, Silene italica, Silene galataea, Silene longipetala, Silene vulgaris ssp. vulgaris, Silene vulgaris ssp. macrocarpa, Silene vulgaris ssp. commutata, Silene kotschyi var. maritima, Silene rubella, Silene fuscata, Silene aegyptiaca, Silene fraudatrix, Silene sedoides, Silene cretica, Silene gemmata, Silene behen, Silene papillosa, Silene dichotoma ssp. racemosa, Silene gallica, Silene tridentata, Silene apetala, Silene conoidea, Silene macrodonta.**

Top: Silene laevigata, a rare endemic of the Troodos Range. Bottom: Silene colorata. A common species in Cyprus as well as in other countries of the Mediterranean region.

Minuartia sintenisii

A dwarf annual, with few erect stems. Leaves linear-subulate, opposite. Sepals with a very narrow hyaline margin. Petals up to 12 mm. long, white, entire or slightly emarginate. This species is an endemic of the summits of the Troodos Range. Flowers April-June.

Other members of the Minuartia genus found in Cyprus are **Minuartia geniculata, Minuartia picta, Minuartia globulosa, Minuartia intermedia, Minuartia thymifolia, Minuartia subtilis ssp. filicaulis, Minuartia hybrida, Minuartia mediterranea.**

Cerastium fragillimum

A glandular annual, with stems 4-10 cm. high. Flowers small; sepals densely glandular. This species grows in the Troodos Range. Flowers April-June.

Other species belonging to the Cerastium genus which grow in Cyprus are **Cerastium semidecandrum, Cerastium dubium, Cerastium illyricum ssp. pilosum, Cerastium dichotomum, Cerastium glomeratum, Cerastium brachypetalum ssp. roeseri.**

Top: The lovely flowers of Minuartia sintenisii, one of the many species endemic to the Troodos Range, emerge from serpentine-rocks. Bottom: Cerastium fragillimum, another rare plant of Cyprus.

Other members of the Caryophyllaceae Family growing in Cyprus are the following: **Holosteum umbellatum, Stellaria media, Sagina apetala, Sagina maritima, Spergularia diandra, Spergularia bocconii, Spergularia marina, Polycarpon tetraphyllum, Velezia rigida, Dianthus tripunctatus, Dianthus strictus var. troodi, Dianthus cyprius, Kohlrauschia velutina, Petrorhagia cretica, Gypsophila pilosa, Saponaria cypria, Vaccaria pyramidata.**

17. Illecebraceae Family

Paronychia argentea

A dwarf plant, perennial, many-branched. Flowers small, in dense clusters. Sepals 5, translucent-hyaline; petals absent. Leaves small, oblong to obovate, opposite, sparsely strigose. Fairly common in rocky places. Flowers December-July.

Other members of the Illecebraceae Family found in Cyprus: **Paronychia macrosepala, Herniaria cinerea, Herniaria hirsuta, Herniaria micrantha, Pteranthus dichotomus, Scleranthus annuus.**

18. Portulacaceae Family

Portulaca oleracea (Andrakla or Glistrída)

A succulent annual. Leaves oblong-cuneate, 5-50 mm. long. Flowers small, yellow, with 5-6 petals. Common in irrigated fields. Flowers in summer.

Top: Paronychia argentea is a curious dwarf plant with apetalous flowers. Bottom: Portulaca oleracea, known by its common names of Andrakla or Glistrída, is often used as a salad herb.

19. Tamaricaceae Family

Tamarix hampeana

One of the loveliest members of the Tamarix genus. Flowers are small, pink, forming dense racemes. Leaves are small, bract-like. This shrub may grow to 7 m. in height. It grows on the banks of streams and near marshes. Rare, in the region of Panagra. Flowers March-April.

Other species of the same genus found in Cyprus: **Tamarix tetragyna, Tamarix tetrandra, Tamarix smyrnensis.**

20. Elatinaceae Family

Only one species belonging to this family exists in Cyprus, **Elatine macropoda.**

21. Guttiferae Family

Hypericum perforatum

A plant with a perennial root. Stem erect, rigid, up to 110 cm. high, 2-lined. Leaves opposite, small, linear. Inflorescence large, many-flowered. Flowers have 5 sepals and 5 petals, yellow, 8-15 mm. long. Stamens numerous, yellow. Grows in the regions of Akamas, Troodos and Pendadahtilos. Flowers June-July. Powder extracted from this medicinal plant is used to promote healing of wounds.

Top: Tamarix hampeana, one of the most beautiful species of its genus. Bottom: the medicinal plant Hypericum perforatum.

Hypericum perfoliatum

Similar to **Hypericum** perforatum, but inflorescences contain fewer and somewhat larger flowers. Leaves larger (13-60 mm. long), triangular-lanceolate, usually amplexicaul. Rare in the Troodos Range, in the area of Agios Theodoros. Flowers April-June.

Other species of Hypericum found in Cyprus: **Hypericum hircinum, Hypericum empetrifolium, Hypericum confertum, Hypericum lanuginosum, Hypericum repens, Hypericum triquetrifolium.**

22. Malvaceae Family

Alcea rosea (Dendromolóha)

A plant with a perennial root and tall stem, up to 1,5 m. or more in height. Flowers large (7-10 cm. diam.), usually pink, but often purple, white or crimson. Leaves palmately lobed, pilose. This species is planted in gardens in Cyprus, but also grows wild in various places around inhabited areas.

Other species of the Malvaceae Family growing in Cyprus: **Althea hirsuta, Althea setosa, Lavatera cretica, Lavatera bryoniifolia, Lavatera punctata, Malva cretica, Malva aegyptia, Malva sylvestris, Malva nicaeënsis, Malva neglecta, Malva parviflora, Malvella sherardiana, Hibiscus trionum.**

Top: the species Hypericum perfoliatum, rare in Cyprus. Bottom: Alcea rosea (Dendromolóha) which may be found growing at the sides of roads, in hedges and in gardens.

22 a. Sterculiaceae Family

This family is represented in Cyprus by only one species of tree, the Australian **Brachychiton populneus,** planted in towns and villages.

23. Tiliaceae Family

This family includes the species **Corchorus olitorius** and **Corchorus trilocularis,** tropical plants cultivated for ornament.

24. Linaceae Family

Representatives of this family in Cyprus are the following: **Linum bienne, Linum usitatissimum, Linum pubescens, Linum trigynum, Linum corymbulosum, Linum strictum, Linum maritimum, Linum nodiflorum.**

25. Zygophyllaceae Family

Peganum harmala

A perennial with many stems up to 1 m. high. Leaves alternate, glaucous, palmatisect, divided into linear lobes. Flowers on long peduncles. Petals 5, whitish-green. Sepals 5, linear. Stamens 10. This species has been found in the regions of Paphos, Famagusta, and Nicosia, but not recently. A medicinal plant. Flowers April-June.

Opposite page: Peganum harmala, a medicinal plant which grows in lowlands and near the sea.

Other members of the Zygophyllaceae Family which grow in Cyprus: **Zygophyllum album, Tribulus terrestris, Fagonia cretica.**

26. Geraniaceae Family

Erodium malacoides

Annual, strigose-glandular. Stems 10-40 cm. high. Leaves ovate-cordate, 1,5-6 cm. long. Lower leaves obscurely pinnatifid. Flowers small, purple-mauve, in axillary umbels. Found in cultivated fields and waste ground in lowlands, sub-montane and montane zones. Flowers January-May.

Erodium moschatum

Annual or biennial, strigose-glandular, robust. Stems up to 50 cm. high. Leaves 10-30 cm. long, pinnate, with leaflets serrate-dentate. Flowers small, pink or light mauve, in axillary umbels. Grows in fields and gardens at low altitudes. Flowers January-June.

Other representatives of genus Erodium in Cyprus: **Erodium cicutarium, Erodium ciconium, Erodium gruinum, Erodium botrys, Erodium laciniatum, Erodium crassifolium.**

Top: Erodium malacoides. Bottom: Erodium moschatum. Both species are quite common in Cyprus.

Geranium tuberosum

Plant with a globose tuberous perennial rhizome. Stems unbranched. Leaves all basal, palmatisect, divided almost to the base into numerous linear lobes. Flowers large (18-20 mm. diam.) with 5 petals, pink, darkly veined. Sepals 5, pubescent. Flowers crowded into terminal umbels.

Other members of the Geranium genus growing in Cyprus are **Geranium pusillum, Geranium rotundifolium, Geranium dissectum, Geranium columbinum, Geranium purpureum, Geranium lucidum.**

27. Oxalidaceae Family

Oxalis pes-caprae (Xiníthra)

A plant with perennial underground stems which produce small bulbs and arise from a tuber 2-3 cm. long. Leaves 3-foliolate, with obcordate leaflets, attached to stem by long petioles. Flowers large (1-1,3 cm.) with 5 yellow petals and 5 small sepals. A native of South Africa, this species has become naturalised in Cyprus, whence it was first recorded in 1880. Grows in fields and orchards at low altitudes. Flowers December-May.

One other species of Oxalis exists in Cyprus, **Oxalis corniculata.**

Top: Geranium tuberosum. Bottom: Oxalis pes-caprae, known by its common name of Xiníthra or Xinístra.

28. Rutaceae Family

Ruta chalepensis (Agriopíganos)

A foetid-smelling plant, perennial with impari-bipinnate leaves and co-rymbose many-flowered inflorescences. Flowers have 4 sepals and 4 petals and are yellow, with fringed margins. A common species on rocky ground in Akamas, Karpassia and the Pendadahtilos Range. Flowers February-May.

Haplophyllum buxbaumii, a member of the same family, also grows in Cyprus.

28a. Simaroubaceae Family

Only one species belonging to this family grows in Cyprus, the well-known tree **Ailanthus altissima (Vromoússa),** a native of China.

28b. Meliaceae Family

The small tree **Melia azedarach,** a native of India, is cultivated in Cyprus, where it has become semi-naturalised.

Opposite page: Ruta chalepensis, or Ágrios apíganos, is well-known on account of its strong smell. It grows on limestone formations in the Pendadahtilos Range, in Karpassia and in certain places in Akamas.

29. Rhamnaceae Family

Rhamnus alaternus (Ramnos or Hrissóxilo)

An evergreen bush with alternate leaves, ovate or elliptical, 2-4 cm. long. Flowers dioecious, small, with 4-5 petals. Fruit a small black drupe (4-6 mm. long). Grows in the regions of Akamas, Karpassia and Kyrenia. Rare at lower altitudes in the Troodos Range.

One other species of Rhamnus, **Rhamnus oleoides ssp. graecus**, grows in Cyprus.

Zizyphus lotus (Paloúra)

A thorny bush. Leaves oblong with 3 longitudinal nerves, 1-2 cm. long. Petals 5, sepals 5, flowers very small. Fruit a fleshy, sweet, yellow or brown drupe, 1-1,5 cm. diam., known in Cyprus as a "kónaro". Branches of this bush are often used in Cyprus to make fences around grape orchards and sheep-pens. Grows in the regions of Limassol, Karpassia and Kyrenia.

Other members of the Rhamnaceae Family growing in Cyprus are **Zizyphus spina-Christi, Zizyphus zizyphus** and **Paliurus spina-Christi.**

Top: Ramnos or Hrissóxilo (Rhamnus alaternus). Bottom: Paloúra (Zizyphus lotus).

30. Vitaceae Family

Only one species, **Vitis vinifera,** grows in Cyprus, in its wild form and as a vine cultivated for its fruit, the grape.

30a. Sapindaceae Family

Various members of this family have been introduced and are cultivated in Cyprus. Among them are **Dodonaea viscosa, Cardiospermum halicacabum, Sapindus mukorossi** and **Koelreuteria paniculata.**

31. Aceraceae Family

Acer obtusifolium (Sfendami tis Kíprou)

A small evergreen tree, up to 10 m. high. Leaves opposite, rigid, 4-5 cm. long, ovate-orbiculate, dentate or shallowly three-lobed. Flowers small; fruit a 2-winged samara. Found in forests and maquis in the regions of Akamas, Troodos, Pendadahtilos and Karpassia.

32. Anacardiaceae Family

Pistacia lentiscus (Skínos or Stsinia)

An evergreen shrub with aromatic paripinnate leaves. Flowers small, dioecious. Fruit a small, reddish, globose drupe. Common in lowland maquis.

Top: Acer obtusifolium. Branch with leaves and fruit. Bottom: Pistacia lentiscus. Leaves and male inflorescences.

Pistacia terebinthus (Agriotsikoudia or Tremithkia)

A deciduous shrub or small tree, dioiecious, with imparipinnate leaves. Fruit a reddish, globose, hard drupe, 5-7 mm. long. Known as "tremíthkia" the Cypriots used to eat the fruits roasted and salted, like peanuts. They also yield terebinth oil, a medicinal oil, also used as a comestible or for burning in lamps. The tender stems of this plant are often pickled.

Another species of the Pistacia genus growing in Cyprus is **Pistacia atlantica,** a robust tree up to 10 m. high.

Two other species growing in Cyprus are members of the Anacardiaceae Family: **Schinus molle,** cultivated as a street tree and **Rhus coriaria** (Soumaki or Roúdi), common in the Troodos Range.

33. Leguminosae Family

Anagyris foetida (Anagíri or Arkolouvia)

A malodorous shrub, up to 3 m. high. Leaves 3-foliolate, with elliptical leaflets. Flowers greenish-yellow, in axillary racemes; corolla much smaller than wings and keel. Pod 10-18 cm. long. Common in the Troodos and Pendadahtilos Ranges. Also grows in Paphos and Amathoúnda. Flowers January-April.

Top: leaves and fruits of the Tremithkia (Pistacia terebinthus). Bottom: leaves and flowers of the Arkolouvia (Anagyris foetida).

Lupinus angustifolius

Annual, 10-50 cm. high. Leaves palmately 5-6-foliolate, leaflets ligulate, 10-50 mm. long. Flowers small, blue, crowded into a terminal raceme. Common in fields in the sub-montane zone (700-1.300 m. alt.), in the Troodos Range. Flowers April-May.

The species **Lupinus micranthus** also grows in Cyprus.

Trigonella balansae

An annual plant with trifoliolate leaves. Leaflets oblong-obovate, 12-22 mm. long. Flowers bright yellow, small, forming a dense raceme on a rather long axillary peduncle. Pods oblong, upcurved. Found in fields and waste ground in the region of Nicosia. Flowers March-June.

Other members of the Trigonella genus found in Cyprus: **Trigonella sprunerana, Trigonella strangulata, Trigonella spinosa, Trigonella spicata, Trigonella monspeliaca, Trigonella cariensis, Trigonella foenum-graecum, Trigonella berythea.**

Top: The racemes of Lupinus angustifolius with their bright blue flowers are a lovely sight in spring, in fields of the sub-montane zone. Bottom: Trigonella balansae is quite common in the rest of the Mediterranean area, but rare in Cyprus.

Trifolium hirtum

A pilose annual. Leaves trifoliolate, leaflets cuneate, apex truncate. Flowers pink or purplish, numerous, small, in capitulate inflorescences surrounded by an involucre of broad, ovate bracts. Common in the Troodos Range, this species has also been recorded near the Mihaíl Arhangelos Monastery west of Stavrovouni. Flowers April-June.

Trifolium physodes

A perennial with stems up to 30 cm. high, glabrous. Leaves trifoliolate, leaflets oblong or elliptical. Flowers pink, in dense, capitulate inflorescences. Calyx inflated. Common in the Troodos Range. Flowers April-June.

Trifolium pamphylicum

An annual, pilose, with numerous stems. Flowers small, in elongate, pilose racemes, pale pink at first, becoming purplish with age. A common species, in fields, clearings and garigue, from sea-level to 700 m. alt. Flowers March-May. See following pages.

Other members of the Trifolium genus growing in Cyprus: **Trifolium pratense, Trifolium cherleri, Trifolium lappaceum, Trifolium arvense, Trifolium angustifolium, Trifolium echinatum, Trifolium leucanthum, Trifolium scabrum, Trifolium stellatum, Trifolium dasyurum, Trifolium clypeatum, Trifolium scutatum, Trifolium striatum, Trifolium subterraneum, Trifolium globosum, Trifolium pilulare,**

Top: the characteristic capitulate, pilose inflorescences of Trifolium hirtum. Bottom: flowers of Trifolium physodes.

Trifolium fragiferum. Trifolium resupinatum, Trifolium tomentosum, Trifolium spumosum, Trifolium argutum, Trifolium repens, Trifolium nigrescens, Trifolium glomeratum, Trifolium suffocatum, Trifolium boissieri, Trifolium campestre ssp. campestre, Trifolium campestre ssp. paphium, Trifolium dubium.

Physanthyllis tetraphylla

A prostrate annual, densely clothed with hairs. Leaves entire, 3 - or 5 - foliolate. Terminal leaflet 10-30 mm. long, much larger than the rest. Flowers very small, pale yellow, with inflated calyxes, crowded together on a common, very short peduncle. Quite common on stony ground and garigue, up to 500 m. alt. Flowers March-May.

Lotus cytisoides

A perennial with prostrate stems. Leaves 3-foliolate, glaucus, more or less covered with silky silvery hairs. Stipules 2, similar in size to the three leaflets. Inflorescences on long peduncles, 2-8-flowered. Grows in the regions of Larnaca, Limassol and Karpassia, by the sea. Flowers March-May. See following pages.

Top: Trifolium pamphylicum, an Asiatic species fairly common in Cyprus. Bottom: Physanthyllis tetraphylla.

Other members of the Lotus genus growing in Cyprus are **Lotus colli-nus, Lotus corniculatus var. tenuifolius, Lotus palustris, Lotus per-egrinus, Lotus angustissimus, Lotus halofilus, Lotus ornithopodi-oides, Lotus edulis.**

Astragalus lusitanicus ssp. orientalis (Pifanis)

A plant with a perennial root and stems 30-100 cm. high. Stems and leaves covered with silky hairs. Leaves imparipinnate, 10-20 cm. long, with 6-12 ovate-elliptical leaflets. Flowers large (2-2,5 cm. diam.), creamy-white. A common plant on the slopes of the Troodos Range, on dry ground and in clearings amongst Pines. Flowers March-May.

Other representatives of the Astragalus genus which grow in Cyprus are **Astragalus echinus, Astragalus cyprius, Astragalus caprinus ssp. laniger, Astragalus macrocarpus ssp. lefkarensis, Astragalus sube-rosus, Astragalus pelecinus, Astragalus epiglottis, Astragalus ha-mosus, Astragalus boeticus, Astragalus sinaicus, Astragalus as-terias.**

Top: Lotus cytisoides, a species growing by the sea throughout the Mediterrane-an, including Cyprus. Bottom: Astragalus lusitanicus ssp. orientalis, a plant known by its common name Pifanis. Outside of Cyprus, it also grows in the Mid-dle East and the southern Peloponnese.

Scorpiurus muricatus var. subvillosus

This species is a typical member of the Leguminosae Family; it is distinguished by its entire, oblong-lanceolate leaves. Flowers small, yellow, forming 2-5-flowered inflorescences at the top of long, axillary peduncles. A fairly common plant at low altitudes. It had never been reported from the region of the Troodos Range before the author of this book found it growing near Platres in April, 1987.

Securigera securidaca

An annual. Leaves imparipinnate, leaflets oblong, rather truncate at apex. Flowers small, yellow, forming 6-12-flowered inflorescences at the ends of long axillary peduncles. Fruit a long linear pod, tapering into a slender beak. Common in fields and orchards at low and middle altitudes. Flowers March-May.

Top: Scorpiurus muricatus var. subvillosus. Bottom: Securigera securidaca, a common species in fields and orchards.

Vicia lunata

A slender annual, with branching stems, 5-20 cm. long; leaves 6-10-foliolate. Flowers 10-12 mm. diam., 2-5 on a common peduncle. Their colour is very distinctive: standards are various shades of violet, wings yellow. This species is typical of those growing on serpentine formations: it is fairly common in the Troodos Range, but completely absent from the calcareous formations of Pendadahtilos. It also grows in certain mountains in Turkey. Flowers March-May.

Vicia narbonensis

A stout subglabrous annual. Stems 20-50 cm. high. Leaves paripinnate, 4-6-foliolate, oblong, 1-7 cm. long. Flowers in pairs in leaf axils, 12-14 mm. diam. Their colour varies from whitish with purple veins to all purple. Two varieties of this plant grow in Cyprus, **var. narbonensis** with subentire leaflets and **var. serratifolia,** with toothed leaflets. A fairly common species in orchards and clearings, up to 1.000 m. alt. Flowers February-May.

Top: Vicia lunata with its characteristic two-coloured flowers is one of the loveliest plants in the Troodos Range. Bottom: Vicia narbonensis var. serratifolia.

Other members of the Vicia genus growing in Cyprus are **Vicia pannonica, Vicia hybrida, Vicia assyriaca, Vicia sativa, Vicia lathyroides, Vicia peregrina, Vicia bithynica, Vicia tenuifolia, Vicia cassia, Vicia cretica, Vicia monantha, Vicia villosa, Vicia palaestina, Vicia cypria, Vicia hirsuta, Vicia ervilia, Vicia laxiflora and Vicia pubescens.**

Pisum sativum (Ágrio bizéli)

A somewhat glabrous annual, up to 80 cm. high. Leaves glaucous, paripinnate, 2-6-foliolate, large, terminating in a tendril. Flowers large, about 2 cm. diam., two-coloured. Standard pale violet, wing darker, deep purple or purplish-black. Three varieties grow in Cyprus: **var. elatius** (pictured opposite), a robust plant with entire leaflets, flowers up to 2,5 cm. diam. and fruits over 5 cm. long; **var. brevipedunculatum**, a slenderer and smaller plant, with flowers 2-2,2 cm. diam., on a short peduncle, and fruit 6-7 cm. long; **var. pumilio,** with flowers smaller than 2 cm. diam., leaflets dentate and fruitless than 4 cm. long. A common species in fields, orchards and forests in the montane and lowland zones. Flowers March-May. Pisum sativum is the wild ancestor of the cultivated pea, which is distinguished by its almost white flowers.

Pisum sativum var. elatius is one of the most beautiful plants belonging to the Leguminosae Family.

Lathyrus sativus (Favétta)

An annual with large flowers, up to 2 cm. diam. Standard almost white, wings blue or violet. Fruit 2-5 cm. long, with edible seeds known in Cyprus as "favetta" or "havetta. Cultivated since ancient times for its seeds, it also grows wild on the island. Leaves have only two leaflets which are long and slender (linear). Flowers February-May.

Other species belonging to the genus Lathyrus found in Cyprus are **Lathyrus ochrus, Lathyrus aphaca, Lathyrus annuus, Lathyrus cassius, Lathyrus cicera, Lathyrus gorgonei, Lathyrus blepharicarpos var. cyprius, Lathyrus setifolius, Lathyrus sphaericus, Lathyrus saxatilis.**

Prosopsis farcta

A small spiny shrub, 20-50 cm. high. Leaves bipinnate. Inflorescences racemose. Flowers small, yellowish-white, numerous, with 5 petals. Grows in cultivated or fallow fields, disturbed habitats, vacant lots in towns, everywhere except in the northern part of Cyprus. Flowers March-May.

Top: flowers and leaves of Lathyrus sativus. Bottom: inflorescences and leaves of Prosopsis farcta.

Other members of the Leguminosae Family growing in Cyprus: **Glycyrrhiza glabra, Ornithopus compressus, Coronilla emerus ssp. emeroides, Coronilla scorpioides, Coronilla repanda, Hippocrepis unisiliquosa, Hippocrepis multisiliquosa, Hippocrepis ciliata, Hedysarum spinosissimum, Hedysarum cyprium, Onobrychis caput-galli, Onobrychis crista-galli, Onobrychis aequidentata, Onobrychis venosa, Alhagi graecorum, Alhagi maurorum, Cicer arietinum, Lens culinaris, Lens nigricans, Lens orientalis, Lens ervoides, Ceratonia siliqua, Calycotome villosa, Argyrolobium uniflorum, Genista sphacelata, Ononis** (12 species), **Dorycnium rectum, Dorycnium graecum, Tetragonolobus purpureus, Aspalthium bituminosum, Medicago** (20 species), **Factorovskya aschersoniana, Melilotus** (3 species), **Hymenocarpos circinnatus.**

Various species of trees and shrubs which have been introduced to Cyprus as cultivated plants include the following. Many of them have been used for reforestation of limited areas. **Robinia pseudoacacia, Sesbania sesban, Tipuana tipu, Dalbergia sissoo, Sophora japonica, Caesalpinia gilliesii, Caesalpinia coriaria, Gleditsia triacanthos, Parkinsonia aculeata, Cassia artemisioides, Bauhinia variegata, Cercis siliquastrum, Prosopis juliflora, Acacia verticillata, Acacia retinodes, Acacia cyanophylla, Acacia pycnantha, Acacia ligulata, Acacia cultriformis, Acacia pravissima, Acacia cyclops, Acacia melanoxylon, Acacia longifolia, Acacia sophorae, Acacia farnesiana, Acacia erioloba, Acacia karroo, Acacia constricta, Acacia greggii, Acacia albida, Albizia julibrissin, Albizia lebbeck, Albizia lophantha.**

Opposite page: flowers and leaves of Bauhinia variegata, one of the loveliest trees introduced and cultivated in Cyprus. It is a native of South Africa.

34. Rosaceae Family

Prunus domestica (Agriokoromilia)

A small deciduous tree with white flowers in fascicles arising on a common bud, on rather short pedicels. The edible fruit is reddish or yellowish-green. Leaves 5-10 cm. long, elliptical-obovate. A common species, both cultivated and naturalised, in the Troodos Range. Flowers March-May.

The following members of the Prunus genus are also cultivated in Cyprus for their fruit: **Prunus armeniaca, Prunus persica, Prunus dulcis, Prunus avium. Prunus avium** has become naturalised by the sides of cool streams in the Troodos Range; it is called Agriokerasia.

Rosa canina (Agriotriandafilia or Arkotrandafilia)

A prickly shrub up to 3 m. high, with hooked prickles. Flowers pink, rarely white, solitary or in clusters of 2-3. Petals obcordate 1.5-3 cm. long. Fruit globose, ovoid or ellipsoid, red, subglabrous, 1.5-2.5 cm. long. A common species in the Troodos Range. Flowers April-June.

One other species of the Rosa genus is indigenous to Cyprus. It is **Rosa chionistrae,** endemic to the Troodos Range, with white flowers and fruit up to 1.5 cm. long.

Top: branch of Prunus domestica (Agriokoromilia) in bloom. Bottom: flower of Rosa canina.

Crataegus azarolus (Mosfilia)

Shrub or small tree. Current year's growths covered with hairs. Leaves 2.5-3.5 (-5) cm., obovate-cuneate, 3-5-lobed, glabrous above, pubescent below. Flowers white, in compact corymbs. Petals orbicular, 7-8 mm. diam. Fruit 1.5-1.8 cm. diam., globose, yellowish or reddish-yellow. Fairly common on slopes at low and medium altitudes, among other shrubs or in pine forests. Flowers March-April. Fruits ripen in autumn.

Crataegus monogyna (Kotsinomosfilia or Mermelitsa)

Similar to **Crataegus azarolus,** but leaves glabrous above and below. Petals smaller (3.5 mm. diam.) and fruit smaller (8-10 mm. diam.), red. This plant is less common in Cyprus and grows only in the Troodos Range.

A hybrid of the two above species, **Crataegus x sinaica** grows in places in the Troodos Range.

Top: inflorescences of Crataegus azarolus. Bottom: fruit of the Kotsinomosfilia. (Crataegus monogyna).

Other members of the Rosaceae Family growing in Cyprus are **Rubus sanctus, Orthurus heterocarpus, Potentilla recta, Potentilla reptans, Aphanes arvensis, Agrimonia eupatoria, Sanguisorba minor, Sarcopoterium spinosum, Neurada procumbens, Pyrus syriaca, Sorbus domestica, Sorbus aria ssp. cretica, Cotoneaster racemiflorus var. nummularius.** Species which have been introduced and are cultivated are **Cydonia oblonga** and **Malus sylvestris**.

35. Saxifragaceae Family

Only two insignificant members of this family exist in Cyprus, **Saxifraga hederacea** and **Saxifraga tridactylites**.

36. Crassulaceae Family

This family includes several species of plants which grow in Cyprus none of which is of particular ornamental interest. They are **Crassula alata, Crassula vaillantii, Umbilicus rupestris, Umbilicus horizontalis, Rosularia cypria, Rosularia pallidiflora, Sedum sediforme, Sedum lampusae, Sedum microstachyum, Sedum cyprium, Sedum porphyreum, Sedum rubens, Sedum caespitosum, Telmissa microcarpa.**

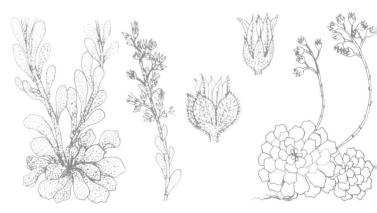

Rosularia cypria and Rosularia pallidiflora

37. Hamamelidaceae Family

Only one species of this family grows in Cyprus, and it is cultivated as an ornamental tree. It is **Liquidambar orientalis,** and has been recorded only in the region of Akamas, near the Andifonitis Monastery in northern Cyprus, and near the Agios Neofitos Monastery in southern Cyprus.

38. Callitrichaceae Family

Aquatic, slender-stemmed plants. Only one representative of this family has been found in Cyprus, **Callitriche brutia,** in spring water in Akamas.

39. Myrtaceae Family
Myrtus communis (Mirtia or Mersinia)

An evergreen shrub, 1-2 m. high. Leaves ovate or lanceolate, opposite, aromatic, glabrous. Flowers white, solitary, axillary. Sepals 5, petals 5, stamens numerous. Fruit a berry, purplish-black, less than 1 cm. diam. Found by streams and in wet places, in many regions of Cyprus, particularly in the Pendadahtilos and Troodos Ranges. Flowers April-May. See following pages.

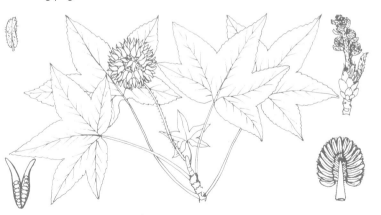

Liquidambar orientalis

Other members of the Myrtaceae Family are the various species of Eucalyptus which have been introduced into Cyprus, either as ornamental trees or for use in reforestation. They are **Eucalyptus torquata, Eucalyptus gomphocephala, Eucalyptus cornuta, Eucalyptus occidentalis, Eucalyptus tereticornis, Eucalyptus camaldulensis, Eucalyptus rudis** and **Eucalyptus melliodora.**

40. Lythraceae Family

Three insignificant members of this family grow in Cyprus, **Lythrum junceum, Lythrum hyssopifolia** and **Lythrum tribracteatum.**

40a. Punicaceae Family

Only one species of this family exists in Cyprus, where it was introduced as a cultivated plant in ancient times. It is **Punica granatum,** the Pomegranate, whose common names in Cyprus are Rogdia or Rovia, valued for its edible fruit.

Top: Myrtus communis (Myrtia) in bloom. Bottom: the fruit of the Pomegranate (Punica granatum) before it has completely ripened, when it will turn a reddish colour.

41. Onagraceae Family

Epilobium angustifolium

Plant with a perennial root. Stems robust, glabrous, erect, up to 1.5 m. high, often even higher. Leaves glabrous, linear-lanceolate 6-16 cm. long. Flowers numerous in elongate terminal racemes. Petals 4, purple. This species is found in the Troodos Range, mainly around Hionistra and Papoutsa Peaks. In the absence of any record of **Epilobium angustifolium** in Cyprus before 1905, it is believed to be an introduced species which quickly became naturalised on cool mountain-sides and along streams. Flowers June-September.

Epilobium hirsutum

A pubescent-villose perennial, with branching stems, up to 1.5 m. high. Leaves lanceolate, amplexicaul, 5-12 cm. long. Flowers pink, solitary, axillary. This plant grows in damp places, from sea level up to 1.600 m. alt. It has been recorded from the Pendadahtilos and Troodos Ranges and from Kythrea. Flowers June-October.

Other members of the Epilobium genus growing in Cyprus are **Epilobium lanceolatum, Epilobium parviflorum** and **Epilobium tetragonum.**

Top: inflorescence of Epilobium angustifolium. Bottom: leaves, flowers and fruit of Epilobium hirsutum.

42. Datiscaceae Family

Datisca cannabina

A plant with a perennial root. Stems erect, 1-2 m. high, grooved. Leaves imparipinnate; leaflets alternate along rachis. Leaflets linear or lanceolate, serrate. Flowers small, yellowish. Male flowers have 3-9 sepals; petals are usually absent; stamens numerous. Female flowers apetalous with one ovary. Inflorescences dense, many-flowered, branched at stem apices. This species grows by mountain streamsides in the Troodos Range, from 700 to 1.300 m. alt. An Asiatic plant, also found in Crete, it is rare in Cyprus, where it has been recorded from near the Kiko Monastery, the Maheras Monastery, near Platanistassa and by the author from the Xeró River gorge. Flowers June-September.

43. Cucurbitaceae Family

Ecballium elaterium (Pikrangouria or Petrangouria)

A perennial plant with prostrate stems. Leaves cordate, fleshy, hispid. Flowers yellow with 5 petals and 5 linear sepals. Fruit oblong, inflated, fleshy, hispid, 3-5 cm. long. The fruit opens automatically at maturity and seeds are expelled with force. Quite common. Flowers January-July. See following pages.

Opposite page: leaves and inflorescences of Datisca cannabina.

183

Other members of the Cucurbitaceae Family growing in Cyprus are **Citrullus colocynthis, Bryonia cretica** and the Melon, **Cucumis melo,** cultivated for its fruit, known as "pepónia" or "pipónia" in Cyprus. It sometimes escapes from cultivation and grows wild.

43a. Cactaceae Family

From this family there are only two introduced species in Cyprus, **Opuntia ficus-indica** and **Opuntia vulgaris**, which have become almost completely naturalised in places.

44. Aïzoceae Family

Mesembryanthemum crystallinum (Bouzaki or Kalia)

A fleshy annual, 10-50 cm. long. Leaves obovate to ovate, with numerous papillae which resemble tiny crystals. Flowers lack petals but have many linear petaloid staminodes light pink or white in colour. Stamens numerous. Rare, near Larnaca. Flowers May-August.

Top: leaves, flowers and fruit of the Pikrangouria or Petrangouria (Ecballium elaterium). Bottom: Mesembryanthemum crystallinum.

Other representatives of this family in Cyprus are **Mesembryanthemum nodiflorum, Aïzoön hispanicum, Telephium imperati ssp. orientale** and the naturalised American species **Glinus lotoides.**

45. Umbelliferae Family

Orlaya daucoides

A small hispid annual, 10-40 cm. high, many-stemmed. Leaves 2-8 cm long, 2-3 - pinnate. Ultimate segments oblong-lanceolate, 1-5 cm. long Umbels small with small white flowers. Some of the peripheral flowers have one petal greatly enlarged. Fruit consists of 2 carpels (schizocarp) compressed, bristly, elliptical, 12-14 cm. long. Grows in the Pendadahtilos Range, Troodos Range and Kalavassos. Flowers March-May.

Pseudorlaya pumila

A plant similar to **Orlaya daucoides,** An annual, but with larger umbels and smaller schizocarps (8-10 mm. long), bristly. Grows near sea shores. Flowers February-April.

Top: Orlaya daucoides. Bottom: Pseudorlaya pumila. These are two typical members of the Umbelliferae Family.

Coriandrum sativum (Kóliandros)

A glabrous annual, stems branched toward the top, 15-20 cm. high. Umbels small, white, often tinged pink. Petals of peripheral flowers much enlarged. Fruit globose, mericarps glabrous, 3-3.5 mm. long. The fruits are strongly aromatic and are used in cooking; their oil is used in perfume-making and distilling, in the manufacture of gin and kirsch in particular. Coriander is also a medicinal plant used as a tonic for the digestive system. Found in gardens, by roadsides and in fields throughout the island, up to 1.300 m. alt. Flowers March-May.

Smyrnium olusatrum (Agriosélino)

A plant with a perennial root and robust stems, 50-170 cm. high. Leaves glabrous, pinnately dissected, not unlike the leaves of celery. It also has a strong aroma similar to that of celery. In former times it was cultivated for its edible stems and root. Flowers yellow, small, in compound umbels. Upper leaves ternate. Grows on rocky ground in the regions of the Pendadahtilos and Troodos Ranges, of Famagusta, Kythrea, etc. up to 800 m. alt. Flowers February-May.

Top: Coriandrum sativum, known in Cyprus by its common name, Kóliandros. Bottom: Smyrnium olusatrum or Agriosélino.

Smyrnium rotundifolium

This species can be distinguished by its entire, almost orbicular, amplexicaul leaves. Flowers yellowish, forming compound umbels surrounded by a pair of perfoliate leaves. **Smyrnium rotundifolium** is rare in Cyprus; it has been reported from only a few places in the western part of the Troodos Range. Flowers May-June.

One other representative of the Smyrnium genus grows in Cyprus. It is **Smyrnium connatum,** an Asian species found in the Pendadahtilos and Troodos Ranges.

Ammi majus

A robust annual or biennial, up to 1 m. high. Upper half of stems branched. Flowers white, in compound umbels, 8-15 cm. diam., many-rayed. Lower leaves are divided into lanceolate-oblong segments; upper leaves divided into linear segments. Scattered throughout the island, up to 1.000 m. alt. Flowers April-June.

The species **Ammi visnaga** is also found in Cyprus.

Top: inflorescences of Smyrnium rotundifolium. Bottom: umbel of Ammi majus.

Bunium ferulaceum

A small perennial plant. Basal leaves divided into linear or piliform lobes. Umbels compound, with few rays. Flowers small, white; petals uniform. Schizocarp oblong, 4-5 mm. long. Found in clearings and fields at low and medium altitudes. Flowers March-May.

Crithmum maritimum (Krítamo)

A many-branched perennial, with sprawling, dense stems. Leaves usually bipinnate; ultimate segments oblanceolate, fleshy, 1.5-6 cm. long. Umbels compound, dense, 10-40-rayed. Flowers greenish yellow. Grows on rocky seashores in the Kyrenia, Paphos, Famagusta and Morphou regions. The tender stems of this plant are pickled, like capers.

Anethum graveolens (Ánithos)

This well-known plant, with its characteristic aroma, is cultivated for use in cooking and salads. Leaves divided into numerous piliform segments. Flowers small, yellow, in large compound umbels. An annual, cultivated throughout Cyprus, it has become naturalised in the region of Nicosia. Flowers April-July. See following pages.

Top: Bunium ferulaceum. Bottom: Crithmum maritimum or Krítamo.

Zosima absinthiifolia

A robust perennial, up to 1 m. high. Stems canescent with long hairs. Leaves canescent, 4-pinnate, ultimate segments small, narrow and dense. The leaves of this plant are somewhat like those of Absinthe (Artemisia); hence its name. Flowers white, small, in large compound umbels, up to 15 cm. diam. An Asiatic plant, in Cyprus it is common in the Pendadahtilos Range and rare in other regions. Flowers February-April.

Lecokia cretica

A perennial with glabrous stems, 40-100 cm. high. Basal leaves ternate-bipinnate; ultimate segments large, ovate-lanceolate, serrate. Stem leaves similar but smaller. Flowers in compound umbels. Petals white, small. Fruit a schizocarp, oblong, 1.3-1.5 cm. long, covered with dense curved prickles. This species also grows in Crete and western Asia. In Cyprus it may be found in the montane zone, up to the highest peaks of Troodos and Pendadahtilos, and in the region of Akamas. See following pages.

Other species belonging to the Umbelliferae Family which grow in Cyprus are: **Eryngium creticum, Eryngium glomeratum, Lagoecia cuminoides, Echinophora tenuifolia ssp. sibthorpiana, Anthriscus caucalis, Scandix stellata, Scandix pecten-veneris, Scandix australis,**

Top: a compound umbel of Ánithos (Anethum graveolens), or Dill. Bottom: a compound umbel of Zosima absinthiifolia.

Scandix grandiflora, Torilis nodosa, Torilis arvensis, Torilis purpurea, Torilis heterophylla, Torilis leptophylla, Torilis tenella, Caucalis platycarpos, Turgenia latifolia, Daucus carota ssp. carota, Daucus carota ssp. maximus, Daucus aureus, Daucus broteri, Daucus guttatus, Daucus glaber, Daucus involucratus, Daucus durieua, Artedia squamata, Bifora testiculata, Scaligeria cretica, Physospermun cornubiense, Conium maculatum, Cachrys scabra, Cachrys crassiloba, Bupleurum lancifolium, Bupleurum subovatum, Bupleurum nodiflorum, Bupleurum odontites, Bupleurum gracile, Bupleurum semicompositum, Bupleurum orientale, Bupleurum sintenisii, Bupleurum gerardii, Bupleurum trichopodum, Apium graveolens, Apium nodiflorum, Ridolfia segetum, Carum multiflorum, Pimpinella anisum, Pimpinella cretica, Pimpinella peregrina, Pimpinella cypria, Foeniculum vulgare ssp. vulgare, Foeniculum vulgare ssp. piperitum, Krubera peregrina, Ferula communis, Ferula cypria, Ferulago cypria, Ferulago syriaca, Opopanax hispidus, Synelcosciadium carmeli, Tordylium apulum, Tordylium maximum, Tordylium syriacum, Tordylium aegyptiacum, Ainsworthia trachycarpa, Glaucosciadium cordifolium.

46. Araliaceae Family

Hedera helix (Kissós)

A perennial evergreen climber. Leaves angular. The long, trailing stems

Top: Lecokia cretica, rare in Cyprus, also grows in Crete and western Asia. Bottom: inflorescences of Kissós (Hedera helix).

have aerial roots which attach themselves to rocks and trees. Flowers are small, greenish-yellow, crowded into globose umbels. This plant is found in the Troodos Range and more rarely in the Pendadahtilos Range. Flowers in summer. See preceding pages.

47. Caprifoliaceae Family

Lonicera etrusca (Ágrio agióklima)

A climbing shrub, up to 3 m. high. Flowers tubular, with 5 lobes at apex of which four are opposite the fifth. Flowers crowded into capitulate terminal inflorescences, pinkish-white at first, turning yellowish at maturity Leaves ovate, elliptical or obovate, opposite, the uppermost connate (perforate). Grows in the Kyrenia, Troodos and Akamas regions. Flowers May-July.

48. Sambucaceae Family

Sambucus ebulus

A plant with a perennial root and robust stems 1-2 m. high. Leaves

Top: The inflorescences of Lonicera etrusca have a pair of perforate leaves a their base. Bottom: inflorescences and leaves of Sambucus ebulus.

imparipinnate, large, with 3-6 pairs of leaflets. Leaflets oblong-lanceolate, 6-15 cm. long. Flowers white, small, divided almost to the base into 5 reflexing lobes. Fruit a berry, fleshy, black, 7 mm. diam. Rare, in the region of Kythrea, where it was introduced some time ago and has become naturalised. Flowers July-August.

Sambucus nigra also grows in Cyprus.

49. Rubiaceae Family

Putoria calabrica

A perennial shrub with woody stems. Leaves small (1-2 cm. long), oblong-elliptical, malodorous when crushed. Flowers pink, small, tubular towards the base, 4-lobed, crowded into terminal capitula. Grows in rocky places, from 500 to 1.600 m. alt., in the Troodos Range. Flowers May-August.

Rubia tenuifolia

A scrambling perennial, with stems up to 1 m. long. Flowers small, greenish-yellow, with 5 lobes, forming lax axillary inflorescences. Common in waste ground and forests, up to 1.600 m. alt. Flowers March-June.

Top: Putoria calabrica. Bottom: Rubia tenuifolia

Other members of the Rubia genus growing in Cyprus are Rubia **tinctorum** and the endemic **Rubia laurae.**

Other members of the Rubiaceae Family in Cyprus are: **Valantia muralis, Valantia hispida, Galium canum, Galium humifusum, Galium setaceum, Galium peplidifolium, Galium aparine, Galium pisiferum, Galium tricornutum, Galium verrucosum, Galium floribundum, Galium parisiense, Galium divaricatum, Galium tenuissimum, Galium recurvum, Galium murale, Cruciata articulata, Cruciata pedemontana, Asperula cypria, Asperula stricta, Asperula arvensis, Crucianella latifolia, Crucianella macrostachya, Crucianella imbricata, Crucianella aegyptiaca, Sherardia arvensis.**

50. Theligonaceae Family

Only one member of this family, **Theligonum cynocrambe,** grows in Cyprus.

51. Valerianaceae Family

Centranthus ruber var. sibthorpii (Analatos or Éros)

A plant with a perennial rhizome and stems 30-80 cm. high. Leaves and stems glabrous. Leaves entire, lanceolate, opposite. Inflorescences dense with purple flowers. Flowers small, corolla 5-lobed, tubular, with a slender spur 4-5 mm. long at the base. This plant can be found in the regions of Kyrenia and the Troodos Range. It may possibly be an introduction which has become naturalised.

Opposite page: inflorescence and leaves of Centranthus ruber var. sibthorpii.

Centranthus calcitrapa ssp. orbiculatus

This species is much smaller that Centranthus ruber var. sibthorpii. It is an annual with inflorescences consisting of few flowers. Flowers pale pink with only a short spur at the base. Basal leaves suborbicular, cuneate at the base. Cauline leaves oblong, often with a few linear lobes near their base. The entire plant is glaucous in colour, often with a reddish tinge. Flowers March-June. This is an endemic form of Centranthus calcitrapa, widespread throughout the Mediterranean area. It grows in the two mountain ranges of Cyprus as well on Stavrovouni.

Valeriana italica (Valeriana)

A plant with perennial tuberous roots. Stem glabrous, often tinged red, 30-60 cm. high. Lower leaves entire, ovate; upper leaves imparipinnate, lyrate. Flowers pink or white, fragrant, in small terminal or laterial capitula. Grows in the regions of Kyrenia, Stavrovouni, Akamas, and the Troodos and Pendadahtilos Ranges. Flowers February-May.

Other members of the Valerianaceae Family found in Cyprus are **Valerianella coronata, Valerianella lasiocarpa, Valerianella vesicaria, Valerianella carinata, Valerianella echinata, Valerianella triceras, Valerianella orientalis, Valerianella muricata.**

Top: Centranthus calcitrapa ssp. orbiculatus. Bottom: inflorescences of Valeriana italica.

52. Dipsacaceae Family

The following members of the flora of Cyprus belong to this family: **Scabiosa argentea, Scabiosa sicula, Scabiosa prolifera, Scabiosa cyprica,** endemic to the Troodos Range, **Scabiosa brachiata, Pterocephalus brevis, Pterocephalus multiflorus ssp. multiflorus,** endemic to the Troodos Range, **Pterocephalus multiflorus ssp. obtusifolius,** endemic to the Pendadahtilos Range and to Akrotiri.

53. Compositae Family

Anthemis plutonia:

A pilose perennial with prostrate stems 6-20 cm. long. Leaves bipinnatisect, small. Capitula 15-20 mm. diam., with tubular florets pink, rarely creamy-white in colour. Ray-florets white, rarely pink, suborbicular. An endemic of the Troodos Range, where it grows from 300 m. alt. up to the highest peaks. It is also found on Stavrovouni. Flowers March-July.

Anthemis tricolor

This species is similar to Anthemis plutonia, but leaves are pinnatisect instead of bipinnatisect. It is also endemic to Cyprus, where it grows at lower altitudes, from sea level up to 900 m. alt. It is found in the mountains above Kyrenia, in Akamas, on the lower slopes of Troodos, near Limassol, Larnaca and Nicosia. Flowers February-May.

Top: the superb endemic of the Troodos Range and Stavrovouni, Anthemis plutonia. Bottom: another plant endemic to Cyprus, Anthemis tricolor.

Anthemis pseudocotula ssp. rotata

A subglabrous or slightly pubescent annual, with numerous decumbent stems. Flowers (capitula) approximately 2 cm. diam. Florets white, oblong. This plant is found in scattered localities around the island, from sea level up to 1.300 m. alt. Flowers March-July.

Anthemis palaestina

A subglabrous annual, with branching stems. Capitula up to 2.5 cm. diam. Disk-florets golden yellow. Ray-florets white, oblong, rather spreading. Leaves bipinnatisect; ultimate pinnules narrow, serrate. This species can be found in fields, clearings, by roadsides and streamsides up to 1.500 m. alt., outside of northern Cyprus. Flowers March-June.

Aside from the above species, the following representatives of the Anthemis genus grow in Cyprus: **Anthemis amblyolepis, Anthemis rigida, Anthemis chia, Anthemis cotula, Anthemis parvifolia.**

Chrysanthemum coronarium (Similoúdi)

An annual, with large flowers, 4-6 cm. diam. and long stems, often up to 1 m. high. Flowers may be completely yellow (typical form) or the ray-florets may be creamy white with a yellow base

Top: Anthemis pseudocotula ssp. rotata. Bottom: Anthemis palaestina.

(var. discolor). Leaves bipinnatisect, ultimate pinnules dentate. A fairly common species, in fields, waste ground and forest clearings at low altitudes.

Another species of Chrysanthemum, **C. segetum,** whose leaves are not so deeply lobed, also grows in Cyprus.

Matricaria recutita or chamomilla (Hamomíli or Papoúna)

An annual with leaves finely bipinnatisect, divided into numerous hair-like lobes. Capitula 1.5-2 cm. diam., disk convex. Disk-florets yellow, ray-florets white. A sweet-smelling plant, used medicinally. Infusions of chamomile are said to be beneficial to the stomach, and compresses of chamomile are used on skin and eye inflammations. Quite common in cultivated and fallow fields, outside of the Troodos Range and Akamas.

Another member of the above genus growing in Cyprus is **Matricaria aurea,** without ray-florets.

Inula crithmoides

A perennial with sprawling stems 30-50 cm. long. Leaves fleshy, linear, 10-40 mm. long. Capitula 2.5-3.5 cm. diam. Tubular florets are yellow and ray-florets yellow, linear, sparse.

Top: typical form of Chrysanthemum coronarium, with entirely yellow flowers.
Bottom: Matricaria recutita (chamomilla).

This species grows on rocky seashores. In Cyprus, it has been reported from Akrotiri, Siriakohóri Paphou and the region of Larnaca. Flowers June-August.

Other species which belong to the Inula genus and grow in Cyprus are **Inula conyzae, Inula viscosa.**

Pulicaria dysenterica ssp. uliginosa

A perennial plant up to 60 cm. high, pubescent-glandular. Capitula numerous, yellow, small, up to 1 cm. diam. Leaves oblong or oblong-lanceolate, somewhat amplexicaul at the base. Found in wet places at low and medium altitudes. Flowers August-November.

Other species of Pulicaria in Cyprus: **Pulicaria arabica, Pulicaria sicula.**

Achillea biebersteinii

A trailing plant with a perennial root. Stems erect, 25-50 (-75) cm. high. Capitula small (3 mm. diam.), yellow, with both tubular and ray-florets.

Top: Inula crithmoides. Bottom: Pulicaria dysenterica ssp. uliginosa.

Capitula are crowded into a dense corymbose inflorescence which resembles an umbel. This species has been found in fields, gardens and by roadsides in Famagusta, Paphos, and most recently by the author in Nicosia. Flowers April-June.

Other species of Achillea in Cyprus are **Achillea cretica** and **Achillea santolina.**

Artemisia arborescens (Apsithia or Sapsissia)

A perennial shrub, highly aromatic. Leaves silvery-canescent, bipinnatisect, divided into numerous linear lobes. Capitula numerous, small, with tubular florets, pale yellow in colour. Ray-florets lacking. A medicinal plant, with properties similar to those of Artemisia absinthium. It is used as a diuretic, tonic for the digestive system, to whet the appetite, reduce fever, etc. This species is scattered throughout the island at low and medium altitudes, up to 1.000 m. Flowers May-June.

Another representative of the same genus, **Artemisia annua,** was reported from a garden in Nicosia at the beginning of this century.

Echinops spinosissimus

A robust perennial with stem up to 2 m. high, usually branched, arachnoid-floccose. Leaves 5-30 cm., green, glandular-pubescent above and

Top: inflorescence of Achillea biebersteinii. Bottom: inflorescences of Artemisia arborescens.

white-tomentose below, 2-3-pinnatisect, ultimate divisions spinose. Capitula large (6-9 cm. diam.), globose, with tubular flowers, pale in colour, almost white and with 5 linear lobes at apex. This species has been reported from the regions of Akamas, Troodos, Nicosia and Pendadahtilos.

Centaurea aegialophila

A perennial with very short stems and leaves spreading on the ground. Leaves pinnately-lobed-lyrate; apical lobe larger than lateral lobes, green above and arachnoid-tomentose below, like the stems. Capitula relatively large, 2-3 cm. diam. and 3-4 cm. high, consisting of numerous pink tubular florets surrounded by spinous phyllaries. Quite common in the littoral zone, throughout the island. This species is also found in southern Turkey and Crete. Flowers March-May.

Other representatives of the Centaruea genus in Cyprus are the following: **Centaurea veneris,** an endemic, **Centaurea solstitialis, Centaurea iberica, Centaurea calcitrapa ssp. angusticeps, Centaurea hyalolepis, Centaurea cyanoides.**

Top: The spherical inflorescence of Echinops spinosissimus. Bottom: Centaurea aegialophila, a rare plant of the Eastern Mediterranean.

Crepis fraasii

This plant has a perennial root and stems 20-50 cm. high, branched in the upper part. Leaves pinnatisect-lyrate, pilose, forming a rosette at the base. Capitula yellow, 1 cm. diam., florets all ligulate. Quite common at low and medium altitudes. Flowers April-June.

Other species belonging to the Crepis genus found in Cyprus are **Crepis reuteriana, Crepis pulchra, Crepis foetida ssp. foetida, Crepis foetida ssp. commutata, Crepis palaestina, Crepis sancta, Crepis micrantha, Crepis zacintha, Crepis aspera.**

Reichardia picroides

A plant with a perennial rootstock and very short stems. Most leaves are on the lower half on the stem. Leaves oblong-obovate, shallowly lobed. Flowers are similar to those of Taraxacum and consist of numerous yellow ligulate linear florets. This species has been reported from the regions of Kyrenia and Pendadahtilos. Flowers February-November.

Other representatives of the Reichardia genus growing in Cyprus: **Reichardia intermedia, Reichardia tingitana.**

Top: inflorescences of Crepis fraasii. Bottom: Reichardia picroides.

Geropogon hybridus

An annual herb with linear leaves. It may be distinguished by its charac teristic capitula which usually have only 5 pink, ligulate florets and 5 lin ear involucral bracts, longer than the florets. Quite common in fields and waste ground at low altitudes. Flowers February-April.

Other members of the Compositae Family which grow in Cyprus are the following: **Eupatorium cannabinum, Bellis perennis, Bellis annua ssp. minuta, Bellis sylvestris, Conyza bonariensis, Evax pygmaea Evax contracta, Evax eriosphaera, Filago pyramidata, Filago erio-c ephala, Filago aegaea ssp. aristata, Filago arvensis, Filago mareot ica, Filago gallica, Phagnalon rupestre, Pseudognaphalium luteo album, Helichrysum conglobatum, Helichrysum italicum, Asteris cus aquaticus, Pallenis spinosa, Ambrosia maritima, Xanthium spi nosum, Xanthium strumarium, Tagetes minuta, Otanthus mariti mus, Tanacetum balsamita, Tanacetum parthenium, Chlamydopho ra tridentata, Tussilago farfara, Senecio vulgaris, Senecio aegyp tius, Senecio leucanthemifolius, Senecio glaucus ssp. cyprius, Ca lendula arvensis, Gundelia tournefortii, Cardopatium corymbosum Xeranthemum inapertum, Carlina involucrata ssp. cyprica, Carlina lanata, Carlina pygmaea, Atractylis cancellata, Arctium lappa, Car duus argentatus ssp. acicularis, Carduus pycnocephalus, Tyrim nus leucographus, Notobasis syriaca, Picnomon acarna, Cirsium vulgare, Ptilostemon chamaepeuce, Jurinea cypria, Onopordum cyprium, Onopordum bracteatum, Cynara cardunculus, Cynara cornigera, Silybum marianum, Staehelina lobelii, Serratula ce-**

Opposite page: flowers of Geropogon hybridus.

rinthifolia, Crupina crupinastrum, Mantisalca salmantica, Cnicus benedictus, Carthamus dentatus, Carthamus boissieri, Carthamus tenuis ssp. foliosus, Carthamus lanatus ssp. baeticus, Carduncellus caeruleus, Scolymus maculatus, Scolymus hispanicus, Catananche lutea, Cichorium intybus, Cichorium endivia, Cichorium spinosum, Hyoseris scabra, Tolpis barbata, Tolpis virgata, Koelpinia linearis, Rhagadiolus edulis, Rhagadiolus stellatus, Hedypnois rhagadioloides, Picris pauciflora, Picris cyprica, Picris altissima, Helminthotheca echioides, Aethiorhiza bulbosa, Hypochaeris glabra, Hypochaeris achyrophoros, Leontodon tuberosus, Taraxacum cyprium, Taraxacum hellenicum, Taraxacum aphrogenes, Chondrilla juncea, Cephalorrhynchus cypricus, Steptorhamphus tuberosus, Lactuca saligna, Lactuca serriola, Scariola viminea, Scariola tetrantha, Prenanthes triquetra, Sonchus oleraceus, Sonchus asper, Sonchus tenerrimus, Launaea resedifolia, Tragopogon sinuatus, Urospermum picroides, Scorzonera laciniata, Scorzonera jacquiniana, Scorzonera troodea.

54. Campanulaceae Family

Campanula peregrina

A perennial or biennial bristly plant. Stems erect or sprawling, 15-80 cm. high. Basal leaves spatulate, up to 10 cm. long. Cauline leaves obovate, dentate, 8-15 cm. long. Inflorescences spiciform, terminal. Flowers approximately 2,5 cm. diam., blue-violet, campanulate, open. This species also grows in Turkey, Syria, Palestine and Rhodes.

Opposite page: Campanula peregrina.

In Cyprus, it grows in cool places in the Troodos Range. Flowers June-October. See preceding pages.

Campanula drabifolia

This is a small annual herb, with slender branching stems. Flowers approximately 1.5 cm. diam., violet. Leaves small, entire or dentate. In Cyprus, this species is found only in the western part of the Troodos Range. It also grows in Greece, western Turkey and the Aegean islands. Flowers April-May.

Other species of Campanula growing in Cyprus are **Campanula erinus, Campanula podocarpa** and **Campanula delicatula.**

Other members of the Campanulaceae Family in Cyprus: **Legousia speculum-veneris, Legousia hybrida, Legousia falcata, Solenopsis minuta ssp. nobilis.**

55. Ericaceae Family

Erica manipuliflora

A small perennial shrub. Leaves linear, very small (4-7 mm. long), in whorls of 4 along the branchlets. Flowers small, campanulate, pink, 2.5-3 mm. long. They form spiciform or racemose inflorescences. Flowers in autumn. In Cyprus this species is relatively rare. It has been reported from the region of Kyrenia and the Kormakiti peninsula. See following pages.

One more representative of the Erica genus, **Erica sicula,** grows in Cyprus, in the island's two mountain ranges.

Opposite page: Campanula drabifolia.

Arbutus unedo (Koumaria or Koumarkia)

A many-branched shrub, 1-3 m. high. Leaves ovate-lanceolate, serrate, rigid and glabrous. Flowers white or pink, urceolate, forming short terminal panicles. Fruit a red or deep red, fleshy, globose, edible berry, about 2 cm. diam. Flowers usually appear in autumn, at the same time that the fruit from the previous year's flowers begins to ripen. This common species in other Mediterranean countries is now extremely rare in Cyprus, where it grows only in certain spots in the region of Akamas. It has been conjectured that this plant is not indigenous to Cyprus, but that in fact it was introduced in ancient times as an ornamental or for its edible fruit and has become naturalised.

Unlike the above species, the Agriokoumaria, **Arbutus adrachne,** is widespread on the island in the regions of Pendadahtilos, Karpassia, Troodos and Akamas.

56. Monotropaceae Family

Only one representative of this family grows in Cyprus, **Monotropa hypopithys.**

Top: The many-flowered inflorescences of Erica manipuliflora appear in autumn.
Bottom: leaves and flowers of Arbutus unedo (Koumaria).

57. Plumbaginaceae Family

Limonium virgatum

A perennial with slender erect stems, 10-30 cm. high. Leaves all basal, forming rosettes. Lamina narrowly spatulate, dark green, 1-4 cm. long. Inflorescences cymatose, with small pale violet or pink flowers. Grows on sandy shores and on saline ground. Flowers March-August.

Other species of the Limonium genus growing in Cyprus are **Limonium sinuatum, Limonium meyeri, Limonium narbonense, Limonium albidum, Limonium ocymifolium ssp. bellidifolium, Limonium echioides ssp. exaristatum, Limonium echioides ssp. echioides.**

Another member of the same family is **Plumbago europaea,** a fairly common shrub in Cyprus.

58. Primulaceae Family

Anagallis arvensis

A glabrous annual, with sprawling, much-branched stems. Leaves opposite, sessile, small, ovate or lanceolate. Flowers solitary, axillary, 8-16 mm. diam., with spreading lobes. There are three different varieties, distinguished by the colour of their flowers: **var. arvensis,** with red flowers, **var. caerulea,** with blue flowers and **var. pallida,** whose flowers

Top: Limonium virgatum. Bottom: Anagallis arvensis var. arvensis, with red flowers.

are almost white with blue centres. Grows in fields, orchards and waste ground, in the montane, sub-montane and lowland zones. Flowers February-October.

One other species of Anagallis is known to exist in Cyprus, **Anagallis foemina.**

Primula vulgaris

This acaulescent perennial has leaves like those of lettuce: oblong-obovate, rugose-bullate, all basal. The flowers, which also arise from the base, are solitary, on long peduncles. Calyx tubular. Corolla tubular toward the base with 5 spreading lobes at the apex, pale yellow in colour. This plant has been reported only from the region of Krios Potamos in the Troodos Range. It is believed to have been introduced. Flowers March-April.

Cyclamen persicum (Lagoudakia or Taousiangoula)

A perennial with a globose tuber. Leaves cordate, dark green with paler marbling above; pale green below. Flowers appear in spring.

Top: Primula vulgaris. Bottom: Cyclamen persicum.

Flowers nodding, on long pedicels. Corolla 5-lobed; lobes oblong, reflexed, white, pink or pale purple, splotched dark purple at the base. Grows in maquis or pine forests up to 1.000 m. alt. Common in the regions of Pendadahtilos and Karpassia; rarer in the Akamas region.

Two other species of the Cyclamen genus grow in Cyprus: **Cyclamen cyprium,** an endemic, and **Cyclamen graecum,** known to exist only in one spot in the Morphou region.

Other members of the Primulaceae Family in Cyprus are: **Androsace maxima, Asterolinon linum-stellatum** and **Samolus valerandi.**

58a. Ebenaceae Family

Two trees belonging to this family, **Diospyros kaki** and **Diospyros lotus,** are cultivated in Cyprus for their edible fruits, the Chinese Persimmon and the Date Plum.

59. Styracaceae Family

Styrax officinalis (Stouraki or Steratsa)

A deciduous shrub or small tree, with alternate leaves, stellate-pubescent, ovate. Inflorescence a 3-6-flowered corymb. Flowers white, corolla campanulate, with 5-7 lobes and 10-16 stamens. Grows in gorges and by streams in the montane and sub-montane zones, in the regions of Karpassia, Akamas, Troodos and Pendadahtilos. Flowers March-June. See preceding pages.

Top: flowers of Styrax officinalis. Bottom: Phillyrea latifolia.

60. Oleaceae Family

Phillyrea latifolia (Filíki or aglantzia)

An evergreen shrub or small tree, up to 8 m. high. Leaves opposite, ovate or elliptical, dentate. Flowers very small, green, axillary. Fruit a black drupe, 5-7 mm. diam. This plant is found in the Pendadahtilos Range. See preceding pages.

Another representative of the same family in Cyprus is **Olea europaea**, in both its cultivated and its wild form.

Introduced species: **Jasminum grandiflorum, Jasminum officinale, Jasminum polyanthum, Jasminum mesnyi, Jasminum nudiflorum, Jasminum fruticans, Fraxinus ornus, Fraxinus excelsior, Fraxinus angustifolia, Fraxinus velutina.**

61. Apocynaceae Family

Nerium oleander (Pikrodafni or Arodafni)

A leggy shrub with bitter, poisonous sap. Leaves lanceolate, in whorls of

Opposite page: flowers of Nerium oleander (Pikrodafni or Arodafni).

3. Flowers large; calyx 5-lobed, corolla with 5 spreading lobes, usually pink, sometimes white or purple. Grows on wet slopes and by streams throughout the island. Flowers May-July.

Another species belonging to the same family was reported earlier this century from the region of Famagusta. It is **Trachomitum venetum.**

Introduced species: **Vinca major, Vinca herbacea, Vinca minor, Nerium indicum, Holarrhena antidysenterica, Ochrosia elliptica.**

62. Asclepiadaceae Family

Members of this family are the species **Vincetoxicum canescens** and **Cionura erecta,** native to Cyprus, and the introduced species **Asclepias fruticosa** and **Asclepias curassavica.**

62a. Loganiaceae Family

Only two introduced species grow in Cyprus: **Buddleja madagascariensis** and **Buddleja davidii.**

63. Gentianaceae Family

Members of this family native to Cyprus are: **Blackstonia perfoliata ssp. intermedia, Blackstonia acuminata, Centaurium erythraea ssp. rhodense, Centaurium pulchellum, Centaurium tenuiflorum, Centaurium spicatum, Centaurium maritimum.**

63a. Hydrophyllaceae Family

Of this family, one member is known to be cultivated in Cyprus: **Phacelia tanacetifolia.**

Opposite page: Heliotropium europaeum (See description on following pages).

64. Boraginaceae Family

Heliotropium europaeum

A branched annual, 15-40 cm. high, greyish-green, clothed in hairs. Flowers white, approximately 1 cm. diam., forming scorpioid, terminal cymes. Leaves ovate, obovate or oblong. This species has been reported from the regions of Morphou and Kyrenia. Flowers April-November. See previous pages.

Heliotropium dolosum

Similar to Heliotropium europaeum, but flowers noticeably smaller, about 5 mm. diam. Quite widespread in the regions of Akamas, Troodos, Famagusta, Karpassia, Morphou and Nicosia.

Other members of the Heliotropium genus growing in Cyprus are: **Heliotropium hirsutissimum** and **Heliotropium supinum.**

Borago officinalis

An annual covered in prickly bristles with an odor similar to that of the cucumber. Stems 10-60 cm. high. Leaves ovate, 4-15 cm. long. Inflorescences terminal, much branched, many-flowered. Flowers blue, nodding. Corolla has 5 spreading lobes. Found in gardens and fields in the lowland and littoral zone. Flowers March-April.

Top: Heliotropium dolosum. Bottom: inflorescence of Borago officinalis.

Lithodora hispidula ssp. versicolor

A much-branched small shrub, up to 1 m. high. The whole plant is covered with hairs. Leaves are small, oblong, 5-15 (-25) mm. long. Flowers small, corolla tubular, 8-15 mm., with 5 apical lobes. Colour of the corolla varies, even on a single plant, from white to pink, purple, blue and violet. A common species in the Pendadahtilos Range and Karpassia: less common on Stavrovouni, in the Troodos Range and in Akamas. Flowers February-May.

Other members of the Boraginaceae Family growing in Cyprus are the following: **Cynoglossum montanum ssp. extraeuropaeum, Cynoglossum troodi,** an endemic, **Cynoglossum creticum, Asperugo procumbens, Anchusa aegyptiaca, Anchusa undulata ssp. hybrida, Anchusa azurea, Anchusa strigosa, Anchusa humilis, Nonea philistaea, Nonea ventricosa, Alkanna lehmanii, Myosotis pusilla, Myosotis ramosissima, Myosotis minutiflora, Myosotis refracta, Myosotis sylvatica, Buglossoides tenuiflora, Buglossoides arvensis ssp. arvensis, Buglossoides arvensis ssp. sibthorpiana, Buglossoides arvensis ssp. gasparrinii, Neatostema apulum, Echium glomeratum, Echium plantagineum, Echium italicum, Echium angustifolium, Echium arenarium, Onosma fruticosum,** an endemic, **Onosma mite, Onosma caespitosum,** an endemic, **Onosma troodi,** an endemic and **Onosma giganteum ssp. hispidum.**

Opposite page: Lithodora hispidula ssp. versicolor, with its colourful flowers.

65. Convolvulaceae Family

Convolvulus oleifolius

A subshrub, up to 40 cm. high, clothed with an adpressed, silvery indumentum. Leaves are oblanceolate or linear. Calyx 5-lobed, corolla infundibuliform (funnel-shaped), a characteristic of the family. Corolla is pale pink or white, 2-3 cm. diam. This species grows near the seashore, more rarely inland, up to 700 m. alt. The typical form, pictured opposite, is found in Akamas, Limassol, Cavo Greco, Nicosia, Kyrenia and Karpassia. There are two other varieties: **var. deserti,** sparsely branched with smaller leaves, which grows in the region of Athalassa and **var. pumilus,** a dwarf plant, with dense branches, in the region of Morphou (Agia Irini). Flowers March-June.

Convolvulus arvensis

A plant with a perennial root. Stems slender, long, trailing or twining. Leaves sagittate, narrow or wide. Flowers 2-3.5 cm. diam., white or more rarely pink. Also to be found in Cyprus is **var. linearifolius,** with sublinear leaves with two narrow spreading lobes at the base. A common species, from sea level to mountain-tops. Flowers April-September.

Top: Convolovulus oleifolius, typical form. Bottom: Convolvulus arvensis, typical form.

Other species belonging to the Convolvulus genus which grow in Cyprus are: **Convolvulus dorycnium, Convolvulus lineatus, Convolvulus betonicifolius, Convolvulus althaeoides, Convolvulus coelesyriacus, Convolvulus siculus, Convolvulus pentapetaloides, Convolvulus humilis.**

Other members of the Convolvulaceae Family in Cyprus are **Ipomoea stonolifera, Ipomoea sagittata,** an introduced species, **Ipomoea purpurea,** also an introduced species, **Calystegia sepium, Cuscuta monogyna, Cuscuta palaestina, Cuscuta planiflora.**

66. Solanaceae Family

Withania somnifera

A perennial subshrub, up to 150 cm. high. Stems and leaves covered with a tomentum of stellate hairs. Leaves broadly ovate, 4-10 cm. long. Flowers have an inflated calyx and a very small, greenish-yellow, 5-lobed corolla. A medicinal plant with narcotic properties. Grows near hedges, ditches, ruins, gardens, in the regions of Paphos, Agia Napa, Karpassia, etc.

Opposite page: Withania somnifera.

Mandragora officinarum (Kalanthropos or Mandragoúda)

Plant with a perennial rootstock, vertical, like a carrot. Leaves large, bullate, oblong or obovate, forming a rosette; stem lacking. Flowers arise from the centre of the leaf-rosette, on long peduncles. Calyx 5-lobed, corolla campanulate, violet, pale violet or almost white. Fruit a berry, fleshy, globose or ovoid, orange, like a small tomato. Grows by roadsides, in waste ground, fallow fields, ruins, in many regions outside of the Troodos Range. Spring-flowering plants in Cyprus bloom early, from December to April.

Other representatives of the Solanaceae Family in Cyprus are **Nicotiana glauca,** an introduced species, **Hyoscyamus albus, Hyoscyamus aureus, Datura innoxia,** an introduced species, **Datura stramonium, Lycium schweinfurthii, Lycium ferocissimum, Solanum nigrum, Solanum villosum,** and **Solanum elaeagnifolium,** also introduced.

67. Scrophulariaceae Family

Verbascum sinuatum

An erect perennial, much-branched, 50-150 cm. high. Flowers numerous, yellow. Corolla has 5 unequal spreading lobes. Leaves covered with a tomentum of stellate hairs; margins undulate or sinuate. Basal leaves oblong or oblong-obovate, 10-30 cm. long. Quite common, at low and medium altitudes. Flowers April-June.

Top: Mandragora officinarum. Bottom: Verbascum sinuatum.

The following members of the Verbascum genus also grow in Cyprus: **Verbascum levanticum, Verbascum orientale** and **Verbascum blattaria.**

Antirrhinum majus (Skilakia)

A glandular-pilose perennial. Leaves ovate or lanceolate. Stems erect, 30-100 cm. high. Flowers numerous, usually purple, more rarely pink or white. Flowers are large with a peculiar corolla which looks like a dog's mouth. The author observed this plant growing wild on rocks and walls near inhabited areas in the Troodos Range. One of its forms, **var. angustifolium,** with narrow, linear leaves in whorls of 2-3, grows in the Pendadahtilos Range and in the region of Kyrenia. Flowers March-November.

Other members of the same family growing in Cyprus: **Scrophularia peregrina, Scrophularia peyronii, Linaria pelisseriana, Linaria chalepensis, Linaria albifrons, Linaria simplex, Linaria micrantha, Cymbalaria longipes, Kickxia commutata, Kickxia elatine, Kickxia spuria, Kickxia lanigera, Chaenorhinum rubrifolium, Misopates orontium, Limosella aquatica, Veronica triphyllos, Veronica hederifolia, Veronica persica, Veronica polita, Veronica cymbalaria, Veronica arvensis, Veronica ixodes, Veronica anagallis-aquatica,**

Opposite page: Antirrhinum majus, typical form, from the Troodos region.

Parentucellia latifolia, Parentucellia viscosa, Bellardia trixago and **Odontites cypria,** endemic to Cyprus.

68. Orobanchaceae Family

Orobanche crenata (Líkos)

A parasite, lacking chlorophyll, which lives on the roots of various members of the Leguminosae Family, chiefly the Broad bean. It is also parasitic on Antirrhinum, Tropaeolum, etc. Stem 15-50 cm. high, pilose. Leaves tiny, bract-like. Corolla whitish, lobes serrate. Grows in the regions of Akamas, Kíti, Kythrea, Nicosia and Kyrenia.

Other members of the same family growing in Cyprus are **Orobanche ramosa, Orobanche aegyptiaca, Orobanche orientalis, Orobanche cypria,** an endemic, **Orobanche alba, Orobanche minor** and **Cistanche phelypaea.**

69. Lentibulariaceae Family

The only representative of this family in Cyprus is **Pinguicula crystallina,** which grows on damp rocks in the mountains, and by streams and torrents.

Opposite page: Orobanche crenata.

69a. Bignoniaceae Family

This family includes trees, shrubs and climbers. In Cyprus its only representatives are the following introduced species: **Catalpa bignonioides, Chilopsis linearis, Jacaranda mimosifolia, Pyrostegia ignea, Doxantha unguiscati, Pandorea jasminoides, Pandorea ricasoliana, Tecoma stans, Tecomaria capensis, Campsis grandiflora.**

69b. Pedaliaceae Family

Only one introduced species of this family is cultivated in Cyprus, **Sesamum indicum.**

69c. Acanthaceae Family

Two species belonging to this family are cultivated in Cyprus. They are **Acanthus mollis** and **Justicia adhatoda.**

70. Verbenaceae Family

Vitex agnus-castus (Ligaria or Ligarkía)

A deciduous shrub. Leaves palmately compound, with 5-7 lanceolate

Opposite page: Vitex agnus-castus, known as Ligaria or Ligarkía.

leaflets. Flowers in much-branched racemes, numerous, small, pale violet, pink or white. Corolla tubular towards the base, with 5 unequal lobes at apex. This plant is found by streamsides and on wet seashores, in the regions of Paphos, Troodos, Stavrovouni, Kyrenia, etc.

Other members of the Verbenaceae Family which grow in Cyprus are **Phyla nodiflora, Phyla filiformis, Verbena officinalis, Verbena supina.**

71. Labiatae Family

Salvia willeana (Spatsia)

A perennial, aromatic herb, with erect stems, woody toward the base. Leaves opposite, ovate or elliptic, 1,5-6 cm. long. The whole plant is covered with an indumentum of soft hairs. Flowers in whorled terminal spikes. Calyx and corolla are 2-lipped. Corolla white, about 1,5 cm. long. This species, endemic to the Troodos Range, is typical of plants growing on serpentine formations. Flowers May-October.

Salvia fruticosa

An aromatic subshrub, with numerous dense branches. Leaves pubescent-lanate, elliptic or ovate. Flowers blue-violet, approximately 1.5 cm.

Opposite page: Salvia willeana, endemic to the Troodos Range.

long. Flowers crowded in terminal verticillasters. A widespread species in Cyprus, in the montane and sub-montane zones, where it grows in garigue and in gorges in the regions of Karpassia, Pendadahtilos, Troodos, Akamas, Stavrovouni, etc. Flowers February-July.

Other species of Salvia found in Cyprus: **Salvia pinnata, Salvia viridis, Salvia aethiopis, Salvia dominica, Salvia veneris,** endemic to the Kefalovrisso and Kythrea regions, **Salvia hierosolymitana, Salvia verbenaca,** and **Salvia lanigera.**

Origanum cordifolium (Kipriakó díktamo)

An extremely rare plant, endemic to the western part of the Troodos Range, to the valleys of the Routhkias and Xeros Rivers. It is similar to Origanum dictamnus, a Cretan endemic, but its stems and leaves are glabrous while those of the Cretan species are covered with hairs. An aromatic plant, its flowers are crowded on a pendulous spike with a large red involucre. Flowers are small, 2-lipped, white. Leaves cordate, opposite, glaucous. Flowers June-August.

Other species of the Origanum genus growing in Cyprus are **Origanum laevigatum, Origanum vulgare, Origanum syriacum var. bevanii,** an endemic, **Origanum dubium,** and **Origanum majorana var. tenuifolium,** an endemic.

Top: Salvia fruticosa. Bottom: Kipriakó díktamo (Origanum cordifolium).

Thymus integer

A sprawling subshrub with numerous spreading woody branches. Leaves very small, linear-lanceolate. Inflorescence a small terminal spike. Corolla tubular or narrowly campanulate, 10-15 mm. long, varying in colour from white to pink and purple. A Cyprus endemic, which has been found in the regions of Akamas, Troodos and Stavrovouni. Flowers March-June.

Stachys cretica

A plant with a perennial root and erect, hairy, tetragonal, robust stems, 60-80 cm. high. Leaves oblong, opposite, 4-8 cm. long, covered with a dense, white tomentum. Inflorescence a lax spike consisting of flowers in 5-10 verticillasters. Corolla pink, 2-lipped, the lower lip 3-lobed. This species is fairly common on hills and slopes in the lowland, sub-montane and montane zones, outside of northern Cyprus.

Lamium garganicum ssp. striatum

A perennial, many-stemmed pubescent plant up to 50 cm. high. Leaves ovate-deltoid, serrate, 1-5 cm. long. Flowers in terminal spikes. Corolla pink or purple, 2 cm. long, curved and deeply 2-lipped at apex. Upper lip of corolla bifid. This species is found in the Pendadahtilos Range.

Top: Thymus integer, endemic to Cyprus. Bottom: Stachys cretica.

Before World War II it was reported from two places in the Troodos Range, but it is uncertain whether it still grows there.

Lamium amplexicaule

An annual with stems 4-30 cm. high. Leaves ovate, dentate. Flowers are pink or purple, rarely white, arising from the axils of the upper leaves. Corolla 2-lipped; calyx tube narrowing toward the base. Grows in fields, orchards and clearings at low altitudes. Flowers February-May.

One other species of this genus, **Lamium moschatum,** grows in Cyprus.

Prasium majus

A small evergreen shrub, with ovate-cordate leaves, 1-4 cm. long. Flowers usually solitary, arising from the axils of the upper leaves. Corolla white, 2-lipped, the lower lip 3-lobed. This plant is fairly widespread in garigue and pine forests. It is absent only from the Troodos Range. Flowers January-May. See following pages.

Top: Lamium garganicum ssp. striatum. Bottom: Lamium amplexicaule.

Ajuga orientalis

A plant with a perennial root and stems 9-25 cm. high. Stems and leaves covered with dense downy hair. Basal leaves oblong, 6-15 cm. long, forming a rosette. Cauline leaves smaller, sessile. Flowers arise from the axils of the upper leaves, forming whorls of 4-6 or more. Corolla small with a long tube, spreading at the apex in 5 lobes, of which the upper is emarginate. Corolla usually violet-coloured. In Cyprus this species is confined to the Troodos Range. Flowers March-July.

The species **Ajuga iva, Ajuga chamaepitys ssp. palaestina** and **Ajuga chamaepitys ssp. cypria** also grow in Cyprus.

Other members of the Labiatae Family growing in Cyprus: **Lavandula stoechas, Mentha pulegium, Mentha aquatica, Mentha longifolia ssp. cyprica, Mentha spicata ssp. spicata, Mentha spicata ssp. tomentosa, Coridothymus capitatus, Satureja thymbra, Micromeria nervosa, Micromeria myrtifolia, Micromeria microphylla, Micromeria chionistrae, Calamintha incana, Acinos exiguus, Acinos troodi, Clinopodium vulgare, Melissa officinalis, Ziziphora capitata,**

Top: Prasium majus. Bottom: Ajuga orientalis.

Rosmarinus officinalis, Nepeta troodi, Sideritis curvidens, Sideritis cypria, Sideritis perfoliata, Marrubium vulgare, Moluccella laevis, Moluccella spinosa, Ballota nigra, Ballota integrifolia, Phlomis fruticosa, Phlomis cypria, Phlomis brevibracteata, Phlomis lunariifolia, Phlomis longifolia, Prunella vulgaris, Scutellaria sibthorpii, Scutellaria cypria, Teucrium creticum, Teucrium cyprium, Teucrium micropodioides, Teucrium scordium, Teucrium kotschyanum, Teucrium divaricatum.

72. Plantaginaceae Family

Thirteen species belonging to this family grow in Cyprus, all of them members of the Plantago genus. Insignificant from an aesthetic point of view, they are known by their common name "Pendanevra".

73. Amaranthaceae Family

Six representative of this family grow in Cyprus: **Amaranthus viridis, Amaranthus retroflexus, Amaranthus hybridus, Amaranthus albus, Amaranthus graecizans** and the famous and very rare **Bosea cypria,** endemic to the island.

74. Chenopodiaceae Family

Salicornia fruticosa

A species growing on seashores, distinguished by its fleshy stems and

Opposite page: Salicornia fruticosa.

tiny leaves and flowers. It has been found in the regions of Akrotiri and Famagusta.

Another member of the same genus growing in Cyprus is **Salicornia europaea.**

The following species, members of the Chenopodiaceae Family, also grow in Cyprus: **Polycnemum arvense, Beta vulgaris ssp. maritima, Chenopodium botrys, Chenopodium foliosum, Chenopodium vulvaria, Chenopodium murale, Chenopodium opulifolium, Chenopodium album, Atriplex halimus, Atriplex rosea, Atriplex prostrata, Atriplex patula, Atriplex semibaccata, Halimione portulacoides, Halopeplis amplexicaulis, Halocnemum strobilaceum, Arthrocnemum macrostachyum, Suaeda vera, Suaeda aegyptiaca, Suaeda maritima, Salsola kali, Salsola soda, Salsola inermis, Noaea mucronata.**

74a. Basellaceae Family

One introduced species belonging to this family, **Anredera cordifolia,** has been reported from gardens in Larnaca, Limassol and Nicosia.

75. Phytolaccaceae Family

Phytolacca pruinosa

An Asian species occurring fairly frequently in the Troodos Range. It is a

Opposite page: Phytolacca pruinosa.

perennial with stems 1-1.5 m. high. Flowers are small, greenish-yellow, crowded in terminal racemes. Leaves large, lanceolate, glaucous. Flowers April-July.

Phytolacca americana

Similar to **Phytolacca pruinosa,** but flowers are violet-coloured. The purplish-black fruit contains a purple juice suitable for dying textiles. Grows in wet places, ditches, by roadsides, etc. in Larnaca and Belapais. This species is a native of North America which has become naturalised in the Mediterranean area. Flowers July-October.

76. Polygonaceae Family

The following members of this family grow in Cyprus: **Polygonum convolvulus, Polygonum maritimum, Polygonum equisetiforme, Polygonum salicifolium, Polygonum aviculare, Polygonum lapathifolium ssp. maculatum, Polygonum patulum, Rumex cyprius, Rumex conglomeratus, Rumex dentatus ssp. mesopotamicus, Rumex bucephalophorus, Rumex cristatus, Rumex pulcher,** and **Emex spinosa.**

Opposite page: Phytolacca americana.

77. Rafflesiaceae Family

Cytinus hypocistis

This plant is a parasite on shrubs of the Cistus genus, in particular on the species **Cistus creticus.** Fleshy, 3-13 cm. high, its flowers have a yellow 4-5-lobed corolla. Leaves small, red, fleshy, bract-like. Grows in garigue near the shrubs on which it is parasitic.

The species **Cytinus ruber,** with white flowers and crimson leaves, also grows in Cyprus. It is parasitic on **Cistus parviflorus.**

78. Aristolochiaceae Family

Aristolochia sempervirens

An apetalous plant whose flowers have a dilated perianth which forms a sort of funnel, strongly curved, brown on the outside and yellow on the inside. An evergreen perennial with cordate-hastate leaves. Grows in gorges, streamsides and forests, from sea level up to 1.200 m. alt. Flowers February-April.
Another representative of this genus in Cyprus is **Aristolochia parvifolia.**

Top: Cytinus hypocistis. Bottom: Aristolochia sempervirens.

79. Lauraceae Family

Laurus nobilis (Dafni or Vagia)

An evergreen shrub or small tree, with dark green, lanceolate, elliptic or obovate leaves, 4-10 cm. long. Flowers dioecious (male and female on separate plants), in dense axillary clusters. Perianth segments 4, whitish green. Fruit a black ovoid-ellipsoid berry, 1-1.8 cm. long. This species grows by streams and on damp ground in the Pendadahtilos and Troodos Ranges, in Akamas and in Limassol Forest. Flowers February-April.

79a. Proteaceae Family

A few foreign species of this family, including **Macadamia ternifolia, Hakea gibbosa, Hakea suaveolens** and **Grevillea robusta,** have been introduced and are cultivated in Cyprus.

80. Thymelaeaceae Family

Thymelaea hirsuta (Fitilíki)

A small shrub with small, bract-like, alternate leaves. Flowers very small, yellowish, with 4-lobed perigones. This species has been found near the sea, on Cape Gata and in the region of Larnaca.

Top: Laurus nobilis. Bottom: Thymelaea hirsuta.

Two other species of Thymelaea are native to Cyprus, **Thymalaea tartonraira ssp. linearifolia** and **Thymelaea passerina ssp. pubescens.**

81. Elaeagnaceae Family

Only one species of this family grows in Cyprus, where it is planted and has become semi-naturalised. It is **Elaeagnus angustifolia,** known by its common names Tzitzifia or Moshoitia.

82. Santalaceae Family

Two members of this family, **Osyris alba** and **Thesium humile,** are native to Cyprus.

83. Euphorbiaceae Family

Euphorbia veneris

A perennial with fleshy stems up to 35 cm. high, with a milky latex. Leaves glaucous, elliptic-lanceolate, 1-2.5 cm. long. Flowers small, reddish or yellowish. The flowers of this genus are singular. Enclosed in a special receptacle, the cyathium, are several male flowers, consisting of single naked stamens and one female flower consisting of a naked ovary.

Euphorbia veneris, endemic to the Troodos Range

An endemic of the Troodos Range which grows on rocky ground. Flowers February-June.

Euphorbia helioscopia (Galatsída)

A glabrous annual, up to 40 cm. high. Cauline leaves obovate-spatulate, 1-4.5 cm. long. Flowers pale green, in large umbels. Grows in fields and orchards at low and medium altitudes, throughout Cyprus, with the exception of the southern part. Flowers January-June.

Other members of the Euphorbia genus growing in Cyprus are the following: **Euphorbia peplis, Euphorbia chamaesyce, Euphorbia nutans, Euphorbia petiolata, Euphorbia heterophylla, Euphorbia dimorphocaulon, Euphorbia hierosolymitana, Euphorbia altissima, Euphorbia pubescens, Euphorbia cassia, Euphorbia valerianifolia, Euphorbia sintenisii, Euphorbia arguta, Euphorbia aleppica, Euphorbia exigua, Euphorbia peplus, Euphorbia chamaepeplus, Euphorbia falcata, Euphorbia herniariifolia, Euphorbia paralias, Euphorbia terracina, Euphorbia thompsonii.**

Other representatives of the Euphorbiaceae Family in Cyprus are **Andrachne telephioides, Chrozophora tinctoria, Mercurialis annua** and **Ricinus communis.**

Opposite page: Euphorbia helioscopia.

84. Urticaceae Family

This family includes the following native species of Cyprus: **Urtica urens, Urtica dioica, Urtica pilulifera, Urtica membranacea, Parietaria judaica, Parietaria cretica,** and **Parietaria lusitanica.**

85. Ulmaceae Family

Celtis australis and **Ulmus canescens** are two members of this family native to Cyprus. We would note that **Celtis tournefortii** and **Zelkova abelicea** were reported over 75 years ago, from between Lefkara and Vavatsinia and from northern Cyprus, respectively.

86. Moraceae Family

Ficus carica (Sikia)

A deciduous tree with a milky latex. Leaves large, palmately lobed. Flowers very numerous. Inflorescence enclosed in a characteristic receptacle which later develops into a sweet edible fruit, the syconium or fig. This tree is native to the regions of the Maheras Monastery, Western Troodos, Athalassa and Loutra Afroditis. It is also common in cultivation throughout the island, in several varieties. It flowers and bears fruit in summer.

Opposite page: fruit of the Fig (Ficus carica).

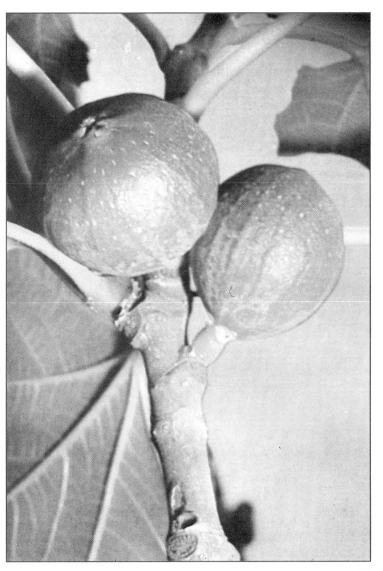

Other members of the Moraceae Family cultivated in Cyprus are **Brous-sonetia papyrifera, Morus alba, Morus nigra** and **Maclura pomifera.**

87. Platanaceae Family

Platanus orientalis (Platanos)

A large, long-lived deciduous tree. Leaves palmately lobed. Flowers in globose capitula, hanging 3-6 along a common peduncle, later maturing into globose achenes. A common species by streams and in gorges in the Troodos Range. It has also been reported from Hrissohoú, Episkopi and Nicosia.

88. Juglandaceae Family

Only the Walnut, **Juglans regia,** is cultivated in Cyprus, in the Troodos Range.

88a. Casuarinaceae Family

Four species of this family grow in Cyprus: **Casuarina equisetifolia, Casuarina cunninghamiana, Casuarina verticillata** and **Casuarina glauca.** They have all been introduced from other countries.

Opposite page: fruits and leaves of Platanus orientalis.

89. Betulaceae Family

Alnus orientalis (Kléthro)

A deciduous tree, up to 20 m. high. Leaves ovate or oblong, dentate, 3-12 cm. long. Male flowers in pendulous catkins. Female flowers in ovoid catkins which mature into cone-like fruit, 1.5-2 cm. long. Outside of Cyprus, this tree is found in southwestern Turkey, Lebanon and Syria. It is common by streamsides in the Troodos Range, along with the Plane-tree (Platanus orientalis). It has also been found in Kyrenia, Episkopi and the region of Akamas.

90. Corylaceae Family

Corylus avellana (Foundoutsa or Leftokaria)

A deciduous shrub or small tree. Leaves large, broadly obovate, almost orbicular, dentate. Male flowers in pendulous catkins. Female flowers very small, developing into hazelnuts, called "foundoúkia" or "leftókara" in Cyprus, enveloped at the base by a membranous, cupular involucre. Rare in the Troodos Range, by streams. This tree has probably become naturalised after having been introduced and cultivated long ago.

Top: fruits and leaves of Alnus orientalis. Bottom: fruits and leaves of Corylus avellana.

91. Fagaceae Family

Quercus alnifolia (Kipriakí velanidia or Latzia)

A large evergreen shrub or tree, up to 10 m. high. Leaves ovate, orbicular or obovate, rigid, dark green above and densely reddish-grey or golden-tomentose below. Male flowers in catkins. Female flowers 2-4, sessile, in leaf axils. Fruit an acorn 1.3-5 cm. long, in a cupule covered with linear scales. An endemic of the Troodos Range, where it grows between 800 and 1.600 m. alt.

Other species of the Quercus genus growing in Cyprus are **Quercus coccifera ssp. calliprinos,** known by its common name "Pernia", and **Quercus infectoria ssp. veneris.**

92. Salicaceae Family

Salix alba (Itia)

A deciduous tree with slender, elastic twigs. Leaves oblong-lanceolate, green above and greyish-green, almost white below. Flowers small, in catkins. Male and female flowers on separate trees (dioecious). This tree grows in scattered locales, by stream and riversides, in the regions of Akamas, Troodos, Limassol, Larnaca, Kythrea, Karpassia and Pendadahtilos.

Top: leaves of Quercus alnifolia. Bottom: leaves of Salix alba.

Populus nigra var. afganica was introduced to the island years ago and now grows spontaneously in various places, by torrent-beds and mountain streams.

93. Orchidaceae Family

Orchis papilionacea

A plant whose rootstock consists of two small tubers. From these tubers, and those of similar species of the Orchis. Ophrys and Dactylorrhiza genuses, a nutricious drink called "salépi" is made. Stem 20-40 cm. high, with 6-9 lanceolate leaves lacking dark spots. Flowers pink or pale puprle with a short ·spur; ventral median petal, or labellum, entire, with dark streaks. A rare species in Cyprus, found in the region of Akrotiri. Flowers March-April.

Orchis anatolica

Similar to Orchis papilionacea, but leaves 2-5 with dark spots. Stems 10-40 cm. high. Inflorescence somewhat lax, up to 15 cm. long. Labellum 10-14 mm. long, 3-lobed, the median lobe emarginate. Flowers pink, purple, rarely almost white. The labellum has numerous purple spots in the center. Spur long, slender, horizontal or curved upwards.
Found in the Pendadahtilos Range. Flowers March-May.

Top: Orchis papilionacea. Bottom: Orchis anatolica.

Orchis anatolica var. troodi

Similar to Orchis anatolica, but taller, up to 50 cm. high. Inflorescence up to 20 cm. long; flowers often secund. Labellum larger and spur longer, sharply curved upwards. This variety is endemic to Cyprus, where it grows in the Troodos Range and on Stavrovouni.

Orchis laxiflora

A tall plant, 30-80 cm. high. Leaves narrow, erect, unspotted. Inflorescence lax. Flowers pink-purple; labellum 3-lobed, with middle lobe much shorter than lateral lobes. A wetland plant, it grows by the sides of streams, small rivers and in marshes. It has been found in the regions of Akamas, Troodos, in Perapedi and some time ago near Nicosia.

Orchis palustris

Similar to Orchis laxiflora. Leaves unspotted. Inflorescence denser, flowers more numerous. Labellum 3-lobed, the middle lobe longer, emarginate. This species has been reported from Fini, Limassol and Dikomo, where it grows in marshes and by riversides. Flowers April-June. See following pages.

Top: Orchis anatolica var. troodi. Bottom: Orchis laxiflora.

Other species of the Orchis genus which grow in Cyprus are **Orchis quadripunctata, Orchis collina, Orchis morio ssp. picta, Orchis punctulata, Orchis coriophora ssp. fragrans, Orchis sancta, Orchis italica** and **Orchis simia.**

Ophrys sphegodes ssp. mammosa

The plants of the Ophrys genus are very similar to those of the Orchis genus. They differ in their flowers, which lack spurs. The labellum is very dissimilar to the other parts of the perianth: its shape and colours mimic various insects. The plant pictured here is distinguished by its broad labellum with pronounced, mammiform lateral protuberances, and its greenish sepals. Fairly common in garigue and in pine forests from sea level up to 700 m. alt. Flowers March-May.

Ophrys kotschyi

A rare plant, its flowers distinguished by their elongate labella, 15-20 mm. long with brightly coloured patterns, and by its greenish-white sepals. It is considered a Cyprus endemic, although it has recently been reported from southern Turkey. Grows in the regions of Pendadahtilos, Kyrenia and Karpassia. Rarer in southern Cyprus. Flowers March-April. See following pages.

Top: Orchis palustris. Bottom: Ophrys sphegodes ssp. mammosa

Other members of the Ophrys genus growing in Cyprus: **Ophrys fusca ssp. fusca, Ophrys fusca ssp. fleischmannii, Ophrys fusca ssp. iricolor, Ophrys lutea ssp. galilaea, Ophrys bornmuelleri ssp. bornmuelleri, Ophrys bornmuelleri ssp. grandiflora, Ophrys sphegodes ssp. sphegodes, Ophrys sphegodes ssp. transhyrcana, Ophrys apifera, Ophrys argolica ssp. elegans, Ophrys scolopax, Ophrys umbilicata ssp. umbilicata, Ophrys attica.**

Cephalanthera longifolia

Leaves without dark spots, oblong, narrow, acute. Rhizome perennial, consisting of numerous fleshy roots. Flowers white in erect spikes. Perianth segments converging, partially concealing the labellum. This plant is very rare in Cyprus; it has been reported only twice. See following pages.

Other species of the same genus growing in Cyprus are **Cephalanthera damasonium** and **Cephalanthera rubra,** both confined to the Troodos Range.

Opposite page: flower of Ophrys kotschyi.

Epipactis veratrifolia

A plant with a perennial root and robust stem, 20-120 cm. high. Leaves lanceolate, greenish. Flowers green-brown. Perianth segments spreading. A rare African and Asian species which in Cyprus grows only on the central summits of the Troodos Range, in gorges and by streams. Flowers May-July.

Other species belonging to the Epipactis genus growing in Cyprus are the following: **Epipactis troodi, Epipactis microphylla, Epipactis condensata** and **Epipactis helleborine.**

Barlia robertiana

A plant with a robust stem, 30-60 cm. high. Its root consists of two tubers, like those of the Orchis genus. Flowers in a dense raceme, greenish, greenish-pink or greenish-white. Labellum 3-lobed, median lobe bilobed. Leaves large, broad, lanceolate, erect. Grows in grassy places, clearings, garigue, by roadsides. Occurs sporadically in various locales. Flowers February-March. See following pages.

Top: inflorescence of Cephalanthera longifolia, rare in Cyprus. Bottom: flower of Epipactis veratrifolia.

Dactylorhiza romana

This plant is similar to an orchid, but tubers are attenuated, with finger-like projections, from which the genus takes its name. Flowers similar to those of the Orchis genus. In this species, their colour varies from pink to yellowish-white. The stem does not exceed 30 cm. in height. Leaves linear-lanceolate, 4-7 (10), unspotted. This species grows in dry places, garigue and pine forests. Flowers March-May.

Another representative of the Dactylorhiza genus grows in Cyprus. It is **Dactylorhiza iberica,** found in wet places in the Troodos Range.

Other species of the Orchidaceae Family in Cyprus are **Neotinea maculata, Acerus anthropophorum, Anacamptis pyramidalis, Platanthera chlorantha ssp. chlorantha, Platanthera chlorantha ssp. holmboei, Serapias vomeracea ssp. orientalis, Serapias vomeracea ssp. laxiflora, Limodorum abortivum,** and **Spiranthes spiralis.**

Top: Barlia robertiana. Bottom: Dactylorhiza romana

93a. Musaceae Family

Representative of this family in Cyprus is a single species, or rather various hybrids of the **Musa** genus cultivated for their fruit, the banana.

94. Iridaceae Family

Gynandriris sisyrinchium (Melanoúdkia)

Plant with a small corm, clothed with a fibrous tunic. Flowers blue-violet, almost the same as those of the Iris, but lacking a perianth-tube. Three of the perianth-segments are broad and curved downwards; the other three are erect, much narrower. Stamens 3, covered by the broadened, petaloid styles, bifid at the apex. Leaves narrow, canaliculate. Grows on dry hillsides and near the sea in the regions of Akamas, Limassol, Dekelia, Kythrea, Nicosia and Kyrenia. Flowers February-April.

Iris germanica

A rhizomatous perennial with a horizontal rhizome. Leaves distichous, gladiate, up to 70 cm. high. Stems up to 1 m. high. Flowers large, approximately 10 cm. long. Perianth segments broad, 3 erect, pale violet, 3 curved downwards, darker in colour. Stigmas 3, petaloid, covering the stamens. Grows in the regions of Nicosia and Kyrenia. Common in cultivation, often an escape from cultivation, by roadsides and around villages. Flowers April-June.

Top: Gynandriris sisyrinchium. Bottom: Iris germanica.

Another species, **Iris albicans,** is planted and has become semi-natu
ralised around the villages in the Troodos Range.

Gladiolus italicus (Pashatiko)

Plant with a corm covered with a fibrous tunic. Stem 30-130 cm. high
with 4-5 linear distichous leaves. Flowers 6-12, secund on a spike, zy
gomorphic. Perianth segments 6, pink-purple; stamens 3. Common in
fields and clearings in the montane and lowland zones. Flowers March
April.

Gladiolus triphyllus, an extremely small plant, usually with 3 leaves and
1-7 pink flowers, is a rare Cyprus endemic.

Other members of the Iridaceae Family in Cyprus are: **Crocus veneris**
Crocus cyprius and **Crocus hartmannianus,** all endemic to the island
Romulea tempskyana, Romulea ramiflora and **Romulea columnae.**

95. Amaryllidaceae Family

Narcissus tazetta (Mitsikórido monó)

Plant with a perennial bulb. Leaves lorate, appearing in autumn. Flow
ers aromatic, arising on a common hollow scape. The flowers form an
umbel; in bud they are enclosed in a membranous spathe. Perigone
segments 6, creamy-white. In the center of the flower there is a golden-

Top: Gladiolus italicus. Bottom: Narcissus tazetta.

yellow cylindrical corona. This species grows in gardens, fields, waste ground, and in clefts in rocks, mainly in the regions of Kyrenia and Pendadahtilos. It is cultivated along with its double-flowered form (Mitsikóri do dipló). Flowers November-February.

In Cyprus, there is also the autumn-flowering species **Narcissus serotinus,** while **Narcissus papyraceus** occurs only in cultivation.

Pancratium maritimum (Krínos tis Thalassas or Krínon tou Gialoú)

A perennial with a large bulb. Leaves lorate, glaucous, appearing in September. Flowers fragrant, appearing in August-September. Inflorescence an umbel on a thick, hollow scape. In bud the flowers are enveloped by a membranous spathe. Flowers are white, large, up to 10 cm diam. Perianth segments narrow, linear. In the center of the flower there is a large funnel-shaped corona, to which the 6 stamens are adnate. This species grows on sandy seashores, but is becoming more and more rare as beaches are exploited for tourism.

Opposite page: Pancratium maritimum.

95a. Agavaceae Family

The American species **Agave americana** was long ago introduced and has often become semi-naturalised.

96. Dioscoreaceae Family

Only one species of this family is native to Cyprus, **Tamus communis.**

97. Liliaceae Family

Gagea villosa

A perennial with two small bulbs, from which 2 linear leaves arise. There are two more leaves on the stem just under the inflorescence, which consists of 5-15 (-20) flowers. Flowers are yellow, approximately 1-5 cm. diam., on long pedicels. This species occurs only on Hionistra Peak in the Troodos Range and on the surrounding slopes. Flowers April-May.

Gagea graeca (Loutia)

This species is distinguished from all the others of its genus by its white flowers, 1-5 on a common peduncle. It is quite common in garigue and forests up to 700 m. alt. Flowers March-April.

Top: Gagea villosa. Bottom: Gagea graeca.

Other members of the Gagea genus growing in Cyprus are **Gagea juliae, Gagea peduncularis, Gagea fibrosa** and **Gagea chlorantha.**

Allium roseum (Agrióskordon or Skortéli)

A plant with small bulbs 1-1.5 cm. diam. Leaves linear-lorate, 10-30 cm. long. Scape 10-55 cm. high, cylindrical. Flowers pink, small, 5-30 in umbels, enclosed in a papery spathe before anthesis. Rare, in the region of Akamas. Flowers March-May.

Allium cassium var. hirtellum

Similar to **Allium** roseum but flowers white. Stems narrower and leaves linear, 8-20 cm. long. This species grows in the Troodos Range. Flowers April-June.

Other members of the Allium genus which grow in Cyprus: **Allium trifoliatum, Allium cupani ssp. cyprium, Allium autumnale, Allium paniculatum ssp. fuscum, Allium paniculatum ssp. pallens, Allium paniculatum ssp. exaltatum, Allium stamineum, Allium ampeloprasum, Allium scorodoprasum, Allium sphaerocephalon, Allium junceum, Allium rubrovittatum, Allium curtum, Allium amethystinum,**

Top: Allium roseum. Bottom: Allium cassium var. hirtellum.

Allium margaritaceum, Allium willeanum, Allium nigrum and **Allium orientale.**

Ornithogalum umbellatum ssp. divergens (Astéri tis Vithleém)

A bulbous perennial with 5-8 linear leaves. Flowers white in many-flowered umbels. This species has been found in fields and fallow land in the regions of Karpassia, Morphou, Messaoria, Kythrea, Akamas etc. Flowers March-April.

Other members of the Ornithogalum genus in Cyprus are **Ornithogalum narbonense, Ornithogalum chionophilum, Ornithogalum pedicellare** and **Ornithogalum trichophyllum.**

Asphodelus aestivus

A rhizomatous perennial. Leaves 1-2 cm. wide, oblong-canaliculate. Scapes robust, branched. Flowers numerous, 20-30 mm. diam. Perianth segments white or flesh-coloured. Grows on barren and degraded land. Flowers January-June.

The species **Asphodelus fistolosus** and **Asphodelus tenuifolius** also grow in Cyprus.

Other members of the Liliaceae Family growing in Cyprus are **Asphodeline lutea, Asphodeline brevicaulis, Smilax aspera, Asparagus acu-**

Top: Ornithogalum umbellatum ssp. divergens. Bottom: flowers of Asphodelus aestivus.

tifolius, Asparagus stipularis, Ruscus aculeatus, Colchicum troodi, Colchicum stevenii, Tulipa agenensis, Tulipa cypria, Fritillaria acmopetala, Fritillaria persica, Scilla autumnalis, Scilla cilicica, Scilla morrisii, Chionodoxa lochiae, Hyacinthella millingenii, Bellevalia trifoliata, Bellevalia nivalis, Muscari comosum, Muscari neglectum, Muscari inconstrictum, Muscari parviflorum.

98. Juncaceae Family

Representatives of this family in Cyprus are the following: **Juncus capitatus, Juncus inflexus, Juncus maritimus, Juncus rigidus, Juncus acutus, Juncus heldreichianus, Juncus littoralis, Juncus subulatus, Juncus sphaerocarpus, Juncus ambiguus, Juncus bufonius, Juncus hybridus, Juncus fontanesii,** and **Juncus articulatus.**

98a. Palmae Family

Various species of this family have been introduced in Cyprus and cultivated, among them **Washingtonia filifera** and **Washingtonia robusta.** **Phoenix dactylifera** is cultivated in many areas, but in the wetlands near Larnaca in particular there are specimens which have become naturalised.

99. Typhaceae Family

One species only, **Typha domingensis,** is native to Cyprus.

Opposite page: inflorescence of Arum italicum.

100. Sparganiaceae Family

In Cyprus, only the species **Sparganium erectum** belongs to this family.

101. Araceae Family

Arum italicum (Drakondia)

A tuberous perennial. Leaves appear in autumn; they are large on long petioles and are sagittate. Flowers very small, yellowish, crowded onto an oblong spadix. Male flowers above, female flowers below. Spadix enveloped in a pale green spathe. Fruit consists of numerous red berries. This species has been found in Lapithos and Fini. Flowers April-May. See this and preceding page.

Other species of Arum in Cyprus are: **Arum dioscoridis, Arum conophalloides, Arum hygrophilum** and **Arum orientale.**

Arisarum vulgare (Koukoúla or Líhnos)

A small plant with a perennial tuber. Leaves cordate-sagittate, 3-7 cm. long. Inflorescence a slender brown spadix, enveloped in a creamy white spathe with brown longitudinal bands, curved downward at apex. This species grows in garigue and on hillsides. Quite common. Flowers December-May.

The following families and species of plant also grow in Cyprus.

102. Alismataceae Family

Alisma lanceolatum, Damasonium alisma

Top: fruit of Arum italicum. Bottom: Arisarum vulgare.

103. Juncaginaceae Family

Triglochin bulbosa

104. Potamogetonaceae Family

Potamogeton nodosus

105. Ruppiaceae Family

Ruppia maritima, Ruppia cirrhosa

105a. Najadaceae Family

Najas minor, presence unconfirmed.

106. Posidoniaceae Family

Posidonia oceanica

107. Zannichelliaceae Family

Zannichellia palustris

107a. Zosteraceae Family

Zostera nana and Zostera marina have been reported in the past.

108. Cymodoceaceae Family

Cymodocea nodosa

109. Cyperaceae Family

Cyperus rotundus, Cyperus capitatus, Cyperus cyprius, Cyperus laevigatus, Cyperus longus, Cyperus glaber, Cyperus fuscus, Pycreus flavidus, Fimbristylis ferruginea, Isolepis setacea, Isolepis cernua, Schoenoplectus litoralis, Schoenoplectus lacustris, Bolboschoenus maritimus, Scirpoides holoschoenus, Schoenus nigricans, Cladium mariscus, Carex divisa, Carex divulsa, Carex otrubae, Carex pendula, Carex flacca, Carex hispida, Carex distans, Carex troodi, Carex extensa, Carex halleriana, Carex illegitima.

110. Gramineae Family

This family, divided into 72 genera, includes many plants which grow in Cyprus. These species are not included in this book.

There are also in Cyprus 19 species belonging to the 9 families of the order **Pteridophyta**.

INDEX OF LATIN NAMES

Abies 90
Acacia 170
Acanthus 252
Acer 150
Aceras 296
Achillea 212-214
Acinos 262
Adonis 98
Adrachne 276
Aethiorhiza 222
Agave 304
Agrimonia 176
Ailanthus 146
Ainsworthia 196
Aizoon 186
Ajuga 262
Albizia 170
Alcea 138
Alhagi 170
Alisma 312
Alkanna 240
Alliaria 118
Allium 306-308
Alnus 282
Althea 138
Alyssum 110
Amaranthus 264
Ambrosia 220
Ammi 190
Anacamptis 296
Anagalis 228-230
Anagyris 152
Anchusa 240
Andredera 266
Androsace 232
Anemone 96
Anethum 192
Anthemis 206-208
Anthriscus 194
Antirrhinum 248
Aphanes 176
Apium 196
Arabidopsis 118
Arabis 112
Arbutus 226
Arctium 220
Arenaria 128
Argyrolobium 170
Arisarum 312
Aristolochia 270-272
Artedia 196

Artemisia 214
Arthrocnemum 266
Arum 312
Asclepias 236
Aspathium 170
Asparagus 308-310
Asperugo 240
Asperula 202
Asphodelus 308
Asteriscus 220
Asterolinon 232
Astragalus 160
Atractylis 220
Atriplex 266

Ballota 264
Barlia 294
Bauchinia 170
Bellardia 250
Bellevalia 310
Bellis 220
Berberis 102
Beta 266
Bifora 196
Biscutella 120
Blackstonia 236
Bolboschoenus 315
Bongardia 102
Borago 238
Bosea 264
Brachychiton 140
Brassica 118
Broussonetia 280
Bryonia 184
Buddleja 236
Buglossoides 240
Bunium 192
Bupleurum 196

Cachrys 196
Caesalpinia 170
Cakile 118
Calamintha 262
Calendula 220
Calepina 118
Callitriche 177
Calycotome 170
Calystegia 244
Camelina 118
Campanula 222-224
Campsis 252

Capparis 120
Capsella 120
Cardamine 118
Cardaria 118
Cardiospermum 150
Cardopatium 220
Carduncellus 222
Carduus 220
Carex 315
Carlina 220
Carrichthera 118
Carthamus 222
Carum 196
Cassia 170
Casuarina 280
Catalpa 252
Catananche 222
Caucalis 196
Cedrus 92
Celtis 278
Centaurea 216
Centaurium 236
Centranthus 204
Cephalanthera 292
Cephalorrhynchus 222
Cerastium 132
Ceratocapnos 108
Ceratonia 170
Cercis 170
Chaenorhinum 248
Chenopodium 266
Chilopsis 252
Chionodoxa 310
Chlamydophora 220
Chondrilla 222
Chrozophora 276
Chrysanthemum 208-210
Cicer 170
Cichorium 222
Cionura 236
Cistanche 250
Cistus 122-124
Citrullus 184
Cladium 315
Clematis 98
Cleome 120
Clinopodium 262
Clypeola 118
Cnicus 222
Cochrunus 140
Colchicum 310

Conium 196
Conringia 118
Consolida 100
Convolvulus 242-244
Conyza 220
Coriandrum 188
Coridothymus 262
Coronilla 170
Corydalis 108
Coryllus 282
Cotoneaster 176
Crambe 118
Crassula 176
Crataegus 174
Crepis 218
Crithmum 192
Crocus 300
Crucianella 202
Cruciata 202
Crupina 222
Cucumis 184
Cupressus 92
Cuscuta 244
Cyclamen 230-232
Cydonia 176
Cymbularia 248
Cymodocea 315
Cynara 220
Cynoglossum 240
Cyperus 315
Cytinus 268

Dactylorhiza 296
Dalbergia 170
Damasonium 312
Datisca 182
Datura 246
Daucus 196
Delphinium 100
Dianthus 134
Didesmus 118
Diospyros 232
Diplotaxis 120
Dodonea 150
Dorycnium 170
Doxantha 252

Ecballium 182
Echinophora 194
Echinops 214
Echium 240
Elaeagnus 274
Elatine 136
Emex 268
Ephedra 94

Epilobium 180
Epipactis 294
Erica 224
Erodium 142
Erophila 118
Eruca 120
Erucaria 118
Eryngium 194
Erysimum 118
Eucalyptus 178
Eupatorium 220
Euphorbia 274
Evax 220

Factorovskia 170
Fagonia 142
Ferula 196
Ferulago 196
Fibigia 120
Ficus 278
Filago 220
Fimbristylis 315
Foeniculum 196
Frankenia 128
Fraxinus 234
Fritillaria 310
Fumana 126
Fumaria 108

Gagea 304-306
Galium 202
Garidella 100
Genista 170
Geranium 144
Geropogon 220
Gladiolus 300
Glaucium 108
Glaucosciadium 196
Gleditsia 170
Glinus 186
Glycyrrhiza 170
Grevillea 272
Gundelia 220
Gynandrinis 298
Gypsophila 134

Hakea 272
Halimione 266
Halocnemum 266
Halopeplis 266
Hedera 196
Hedypnois 222
Hedysarum 170
Helianthemum 124
Helichrysum 220
Heliotropium 238

Helminthotheca 222
Hibiscus 138
Hippocrepis 170
Hirschfeldia 120
Holarrhena 236
Holosteum 134
Hyacinthella 310
Hymenocarpos 170
Hymenolobus 120
Hyoscyamus 246
Hyoseris 222
Hypecoum 106
Hypericum 136-138
Hypochaeris 222

Iberis 118
Inula 210-212
Ipomoea 244
Iris 298-300
Isolepis 315

Jacaranda 252
Jasminum 234
Juglans 280
Juncus 310
Juniperus 94
Jurinea 220
Justicia 252

Kickxia 248
Koelpinia 222
Koelreuteria 150
Kohlrauschia 134
Krubera 196

Lactuca 222
Lagoesia 194
Lamium 258-260
Lathyrus 168
Launea 222
Laurus 272
Lavandula 262
Lavatera 138
Lecokia 194
Legousia 224
Lens 170
Leontice 102
Leontodon 222
Lepidium 118
Limodorum 296
Limonium 228
Limosella 248
Linaria 248
Linum 140
Liquidambar 177
Lithodora 240

Lobularia 118
Lonicera 198
Lotus 158-160
Lupinus 154
Lycium 246
Lythrum 178

Macadamia 272
Maclura 280
Malkolmia 118
Malus 176
Malva 138
Malvella 138
Mandragora 246
Mantisalca 222
Marrubium 264
Matricaria 210
Matthiola 116
Medicago 170
Melia 146
Melilotus 170
Melissa 262
Mentha 262
Mercurialis 276
Mesembryanthemum 184
 -186
Micromeria 262
Minuartia 132
Misopates 248
Molucella 264
Monotropa 226
Morus 280
Musa 298
Muscari 310
Myosotis 240
Myrtus 177

Najas 314
Narcissus 300-302
Nasturtium 118
Neatostema 240
Neotinea 296
Nepeta 264
Nerium 234
Nerium 236
Neslia 120
Neurada 176
Nicotiana 246
Nigella 100
Noaea 266
Nonea 240
Notobasis 220

Ochrosia 236
Octhodium 120

Odontites 250
Onobrychis 170
Ononis 170
Onopordum 220
Onosma 240
Ophrys 290-292
Opopanax 196
Opuntia 184
Orchis 286-288-290
Origanum 256
Orlaya 186
Ornithogalum 308
Ornithopus 170
Orobanche 250
Orthurus 176
Osyris 274
Otanthus 220
Oxalis 144

Paeonia 102
Paliurus 148
Pallenis 220
Pancratium 302
Pandorea 252
Papaver 104-106
Parentucellia 250
Parietaria 278
Parkinsonia 170
Paronychia 134
Peganum 140
Petrorhagia 134
Phacelia 236
Phagnalon 220
Phillyrea 234
Phlomis 264
Phoenix 310
Phyla 254
Physanthyllis 158
Physospermum 196
Phytolacca 266-268
Picris 222
Pimpinella 196
Pinguicula 250
Pinus 90
Pistacia 150-152
Pisum 166
Plantago 264
Platanthera 296
Platanus 280
Prosopis 168-170
Polycarpon 134
Polycnemum 266
Polygala 128
Polygonum 268
Portulaca 134

Posidonia 314
Potamogeton 314
Potentilla 176
Prasium 260
Primula 230
Prunella 264
Prunus 172
Pseudognaphalium 220
Pseudorlaya 186
Pterocephalus 206
Pulicaria 212
Punica 178
Putoria 200
Pycreus 315
Pyrostegia 252
Pyrus 176

Quercus 284

Ranunculus 96-98
Raphanus 114
Rapistrum 118
Reichardia 218
Reseda 122
Rhagadiolus 222
Rhamnus 148
Rhus 152
Ricinus 276
Ridolfia 196
Robinia 170
Roemeria 106
Romulea 300
Rosa 172
Rosmarinus 264
Rosularia 176
Rubia 200-202
Rubus 176
Rumex 268
Ruppia 314
Ruscus 310

Sagina 134
Salicornia 264-266
Salix 284
Salsola 266
Salvia 254-256
Sambucus 198
Samolus 232
Sanguisorba 176
Sapindus 150
Saponaria 134
Sarcopoterium 176
Satureja 262
Saxifraga 176
Scabiosa 206
Scaligeria 196

Scandix 194
Scariola 222
Schinus 152
Schoenoplectus 315
Schoenus 315
Scilla 310
Scirpoides 315
Scolymus 222
Scorpiurus 162
Scorzonera 222
Scrophularia 248
Scutellaria 264
Securigera 162
Sedum 176
Senecio 220
Sequoia 94
Serapias 296
Serratula 222
Sesamum 252
Sesbania 170
Sideritis 264
Silene 130
Silybum 222
Sinapis 114
Sisymbrium 118
Smilax 308
Smyrmium 188-190
Solanum 246
Solenopsis 224
Sonchus 222
Sophora 170
Sorbus 176
Sparganium 312
Sperguaria 134
Spiranthes 296
Stachys 258
Staechelina 222

Stellaria 134
Steptorhamphus 222
Styrax 232
Suaeda 266
Synelcosciadium 196

Tamarix 136
Tamus 304
Tanacetum 220
Taraxacum 222
Tagetes 220
Tecoma 252
Tecomaria 252
Teesdalia 118
Telephium 186
Telmissa 176
Tetregonolobus 170
Teucrium 264
Thesium 274
Thlaspi 120
Thymelaea 272-274
Thymus 258
Tipuana 170
Trifolium 156-158
Tolpis 222
Tordylium 196
Torilis 196
Torularia 118
Trachomitum 236
Tragopogon 222
Tribulus 142
Triglochin 314
Trigonella 154
Tulipa 310
Turgenia 196
Turrita 118
Tussilago 220

Typha 310
Tyrimnus 220

Umbilicus 176
Urospermum 222
Urtica 278

Vaccaria 134
Valantia 202
Valerianella 204
Valerianella 204
Velezia 134
Verbascum 245-248
Verbena 254
Veronica 248
Vicia 164-166
Vinca 236
Viola 126-128
Vitex 252
Vitis 150

Washingtonia 310
Withania 244

Xanthium 220
Xeranthemum 220

Zannichellia 314
Zelkova 278
Ziziphora 264
Zizyphus 148
Zosima 194
Zostera 314
Zygophyllum 142

BIBLIOGRAPHY

Additions to the Flora of Cyprus. Meikle in Annales Musei Goulandris, Athens.

A revision of Papaver Sect. Papaver (Papaveraceae). J.W. Kadereit in Botanische Jahrbücher Bd 108. Stuttgart, 1986.

Cyprus State Forests Map.

Encyclopedia "Domi", entry Cyprus.

Flora of Cyprus, Vol. I and II. R.D. Meikle. Royal Botanic Gardens, Kew, 1977 and 1985.

Geological map of Cyprus. Geological Survey Department.

List of the vascular plants of Cyprus. B.F. Osorio-Tafall and G.M. Seraphim. Nicosia, 1973.

Med - Checklist Notulae II - Wildenowia 15. W. Greüter and T. Raus. 1985.

The Botanical Paradises of Cyprus and the Necessity of Preserving Them. G. Sfikas.